BEYOND 2001

BEYOND 2001

The Laws of Physics Revolutionised

Sandy Kidd

With Ron Thompson

SIDGWICK & JACKSON
LONDON

First published in Great Britain in 1990 by Sidgwick & Jackson Limited

ISBN 0-283-99925 X

Typeset by Matrix, 21 Russell Street, London WC1

Printed by Billings & Sons Ltd, Worcester

for Sidgwick & Jackson Limited
1 Tavistock Chambers, Bloomsbury Way
London WC1A 2SG

'The greatest mathematician who ever walked on these shores, Simon Newcomb, proved in 1903 that a flying machine carrying a pilot is a mathematical impossibility. In the same year of 1903 the Wright brothers, without mathematics, but by a fact, proved him wrong.'

'All fruitful ideas have been conceived in the minds of the non-conformists, for whom the known was still unknown, and who often went back to begin where others passed by, sure of their way. The truth of today was the heresy of yesterday.'

– Immanuel Velikovsky, Russian scientist and writer

'If you have had your attention directed to the novelties of thought in your own lifetime, you will have observed that almost all really new ideas have a certain aspect of foolishness when they are first produced.'

– Alfred North Whitehead, British philosopher and mathematician

Prologue

There it stood, bathed in a pool of angle-poised light, looking like some strange icon in a modern temple. This was the culmination of all my hopes and dreams, nursed and cherished as if a child, until now it almost had a soul of its own. I wondered yet again how such a thing as this could so possess me, dominating my life with all its moods and whims and constant needs. This after all was no human being. It was a machine and I had made it what it was. But in some remarkable, almost mystical, way this machine had become a part of me.

Tonight it stood alone on a workbench in the middle of my lock-up garage, etched out of the darkness by this single beam of light, the silver-grey metal of its superstructure glinting and gleaming under the glare of the lamp. But this was no ordinary mechanical device. It consisted of a crucifix eighteen inches high inside a diamond-shaped frame with a gyroscope, a thick-rimmed wheel four inches in diameter, at either end of the cross-piece. There were pulleys, belts and linkages, ball joints, bearings and couplings. A mass of components lovingly assembled to create my own personal brainchild.

It was with this machine, on this November night in 1984, that I was about to challenge something very sacred. Nothing less than the established laws of physics. I wanted to prove that an anti-gravity machine was possible after all. That the gravitational pull of the earth could be overcome by harnessing other natural forces through a device which would open up the universe and send shock waves through the scientific world. Colleagues and friends had warned me that I was mad to attempt the impossible. Even if by some miracle it worked, they said, the experts would simply dismiss my invention as an interesting curiosity.

Until this stage I had been the machine's master, dictating its shape and purpose in life, patiently crafting each part in the tiny workshop converted out of my garden shed, and then fitting them all together into the jigsaw of my space device. Now, like a child emerging from the womb, it was fully formed with a will and personality of its own. But what had I created? Suddenly I felt frightened and lonely, like an explorer about to step into the unknown.

I turned my attention to the contraption hanging in mid-air from a thick piece of string which had been attached to the top of the machine's vertical shaft and fed along an overhead beam by pulleys before dropping down by the side of the bench. Tied to the end of the string was a chunk of cast iron to which was attached a magnet. Clinging to it were a number of small, two-ounce spanners. I moved the string gently up and down to test the balance of the system. The counterweight was now exactly the same weight as the machine.

I looked nervously at my watch. It had just gone eleven o'clock and lights were starting to go out in the bungalow suburb of Barnhill on the eastern perimeter of Dundee. The mournful howl of a dog in a neighbour's garden was the only sound to penetrate the cheerless comfort of my concrete garage. Drawing a deep breath I leaned across to the wall and flicked on a switch. The machine immediately sprang to life, breaking into a steady rhythmic spin, rather like rotor blades limbering up on a helicopter.

Swoosh . . . swoosh . . . swoosh . . . it went, now a blur of whirling metal. Dropping on one knee I picked up an electric starter from the floor and fired up the model aeroplane engine attached to the bottom of the machine's central shaft. Suddenly the gentle, swishing beat of the spinning device was drowned out by the harsh clamour of the internal combustion engine as it transmitted its power by belt and pulley to the gyroscopes on the cross-piece. These wheels were now rotating as well as the entire machine.

Working with a radio-control handset, I gradually throttled up the engine until the gyroscopes were rotating at 4000 revolutions per minute (rpm). Although the machine had been firmly clamped into position on the bench it had the freedom to rise several inches off the surface. But it wasn't budging. I stepped up the power to 5000 rpm. Still there was no response. Only the clatter of the engine was getting louder. When at 6000 rpm nothing happened, I switched everything off. There should have been some movement by now. 'What the devil's happening?' I muttered to myself, sitting back on my haunches and contemplating the machine as it came to rest.

I decided to go through the checks. First I tested the belt

drives for tension and then made sure the linkages were moving freely. I spun each of the wheels by hand. Everything seemed in order. I gave the ball joints more oil then went through the start-up procedure once more. Within minutes I was up to 7000 revs. Then 8000. The machine was now starting to scream and vibrate with pent-up power, but still finding no release for all its restless energy. It seemed to be glued to the bench. My curse was lost in the din just seconds before I cut power for a second time. Striding out of the garage, I swung the door shut behind me and crunched across the gravel path to the rear of the house.

My wife, Janet, was in the kitchen having coffee and listening to the radio when I barged through the back door and threw myself on a stool at the breakfast bar. 'No luck?' she asked, reading the disappointment on my face.

'Not a thing,' I replied bitterly. 'Not a damned sausage. I can't understand that blasted machine. I had worked out everything so carefully and gone over it time and again. When I think of all the years of effort I've put into that thing . . . ' I broke off to light up a cigarette, then stared disconsolately at the floor.

'What will you do now?' Janet asked anxiously, breaking the heavy silence.

'What can I do?' I retorted. 'I've been through every permutation with that machine . . . sizes, weights, angles, speeds . . . I've run out of options. I'm finished. I'll throw the whole damn lot out in the morning and get back to some sort of normal life again.' By now I was feeling pretty sorry for myself.

'Why not run the thing flat out and see what happens?'

I grimaced. Just like a woman to suggest that, I thought. I dragged heavily on my cigarette before answering. 'If I do that the engine will simply blow up. It was kicking up a hell of a noise when I put down the foot last time. I can't see it taking much more throttle.'

'You've nothing to lose,' persisted Janet. 'Go on. Have one last try. If you're going to pack it in you may as well go out with a bang.'

I stood up, stubbed out my cigarette without speaking, then walked back across the path to the garage. This time I made sure the up-and-over door was properly fastened behind me to contain the noise. It was now after midnight.

I set the machine in motion, started up the gyros, then slowly accelerated through the rev band until I was climbing beyond the previous ceiling of 8000 revs. By the time I got to 9000 the engine was screaming its head off and I was starting to cough and splutter as the fumes and exhaust smoke filled the garage, unable to escape. But still no lift-off. By now I was almost stiff with tension, my thoughts so confused I couldn't think of what to do next. Then it happened. Just when I thought the engine had reached the end of its tether, and I was preparing to abandon the operation, the device gave a final, excruciating howl and glided upwards until it hovered three inches above the worktop. At that point it was restrained from rising further.

I froze, as if I had just seen a ghost. Then, still in a crouching position, I forced myself into action. With one hand continuing to control the throttle, I stretched out the other to pull a spanner from the magnet on the counter-balance, letting it fall heedlessly to the floor. Although the spanner's removal had made the counterweight two ounces lighter, and should have meant the machine dropping back on to the bench, it continued to remain in a state of levitation. This meant that it, too, had somehow shed the same amount of weight.

I could now feel my heart thumping, and my breath was coming in quick gasps, as I plucked another spanner off the magnet. Still the machine remained aloft. Twice more I reached out and two more spanners fell to the floor. But as the counterweight grew steadily lighter the machine was miraculously matching it ounce for ounce until now both were eight ounces lighter and my device was continuing to thrash round in space, roaring its defiance at gravity. Only when I removed a fifth spanner did the machine finally fall back to earth.

I killed the power and rose slowly to my feet. My concentration over those five, dramatic minutes had been at such a pitch that my brain was now in turmoil. This was the supreme moment I had dedicated my life to and yet I was unable to grasp the reality of what had just happened. Then gradually, as it dawned on me, I was filled with an overwhelming sense of relief. Not elation or joy or any desire to punch the air with excitement. Just sheer relief – a deep, inner contentment. Before my very eyes in the early hours of that winter morning my anti-gravity machine had created enough thrust to float a medium-sized orange through the middle of the garage.

I went quickly back across the path to the house. Janet was still waiting in the kitchen. She was always waiting it seemed.

'You've done it,' she announced triumphantly, the look on my face having again told her everything. I laughed. 'What happens now?' she asked, her voice brittle with tension.

'We put on our seat belts,' I said quietly, peeling off my boiler suit. 'We have a stormy journey ahead.'

A short time later I went to bed for my first decent night's sleep in years.

Chapter 1

The exploration of the universe is the last great challenge we face, but one so intimidating that it almost defies comprehension. In fact, I have seen young adults break down emotionally during discussions on this subject when they realize how insignificant they are within the totality of the cosmos. They simply can't handle the truth of something so overwhelming.

To understand the purpose of my machine, the very reason for its creation, we must first consider the sheer scale of the space beyond the boundaries of our own planet. It is not without reason that we apply the word 'astronomical' to anything whose size beggars description.

Take the stars, for example. No one really knows how many there are but they certainly exceed the sum of all the grains of sand on every beach in the world. Yet the universe is so unimaginably empty that if each of these stars was reduced to the size of a ship not one would be within a million miles of its nearest neighbour. In reality some stars are so big they could contain millions of earths and are so far away in other galaxies that their light, which travels continuously at 186,300 miles per second, takes 15,000 million years to reach us.

This makes our own solar system seem a pretty parochial place when you consider that light from the sun needs only 8 minutes 18 seconds to get to us on earth, a mere 93 million miles away. When the American satellite, Voyager 2, reached Neptune in August 1989 to send back the first pictures of our most distant neighbour in our own 'back yard', the 3000-million-mile journey was hailed as a staggering achievement. But the fact is that it took the spacecraft twelve whole years to get there. Imagine going up to the booking office of a satellite transport station and asking for a return ticket to Neptune, only to be told you'll be away for at least twenty-four years. That would be little better than a long prison sentence.

My reason for trotting out these staggering statistics is simply to emphasize how impossible it would be in any case, with present forms of propulsion, for people on this planet to undertake journeys of such colossal magnitude when the present average life expectancy is only seventy-four years. Even if you set out at birth you would run out of your allocated span long before reaching the first star. Indeed, you would be dead within a few years from the severe medical disorders caused by constant weightlessness in the spacecraft. Your bones would decalcify and muscles gradually go to waste. Madness would be inevitable. You would simply become a vegetable.

Distance and lack of gravity are, therefore, the two enormous and inseparable problems that must be overcome if we are to succeed in opening up the universe and reach a fuller understanding of our own existence and that of other beings who may inhabit other solar systems in deep space. But first let us look at the resources we have at the moment.

Conventional vehicles are designed to react against air, water, or solid surface in order to achieve movement. In space, where there is no medium to react upon, and where rockets alone can function, this movement can only be achieved by shedding mass. In other words, a rocket has to burn off enormous amounts of fuel, in effect getting rid of itself as quickly as possible, in order to keep going forward. When all the fuel has been consumed and the rocket has almost devoured itself, what is left, that is the space capsule, will proceed indefinitely through the universe maintaining the velocity reached when the fuel ran out. This is called terminal velocity. In the case of Voyager 2, it was actually able to increase its speed by harnessing the gravitational pull of each planet it passed in such a way that it kept being slung forward. Its speed increased from 25,000 miles an hour when it left earth to 30,000 mph as it rounded Jupiter and reached 34,000 mph passing Saturn. By the time it got to Neptune it was streaking along at 40,000 mph. Compared to the speeds we travel on earth that may seem unbelievable. But it's only a dawdle when you consider the billions of miles you would have to cover to explore the Great Beyond.

Our present forms of propulsion, then, are in strict accordance with Newton's Third Law of Motion which states that the action of a force always produces a reaction in the body and that reaction is of equal magnitude, but opposite in direction, to the action itself. One of the best ways of testing this centuries-old law for yourself is to lay a tray on top of some snooker balls on the ground, then stand on it with a pile of bricks. When you try to move by swaying your body in a certain direction the tray and the balls will go with you. But each time you straighten up, as you must, you will roll back again to your original position. You will never be able to gain ground because you have nothing to thrust against. Now start throwing the bricks away in the opposite direction to which you wish to move. The action of the brick leaving your hand causes a reaction in your body which will propel you across the floor and this will continue as you keep getting rid of the bricks.

What, therefore, is required is a machine which, unlike the rocket or the tray on the snooker balls, will continue to accelerate at a required rate for extended periods without the need to react on anything or shed mass. Such an ideal device, powered internally by a nuclear unit, could well be the space drive of the future. Given such a machine, you must aim to move it through space at precisely the same rate as an object would fall under the influence of gravity. This is known as One G. If this is maintained in the forward direction the machine's velocity through space will theoretically keep increasing at a dramatic rate, making the device go faster and faster all the time to reach speeds never achieved before and believed to be impossible. When you are halfway to your destination, all you would do is to put the One G drive into reverse thrust to make a soft landing on another astronomical body.

After the first hour of forward thrust you will have covered about 40,000 miles; an hour and a half later you will be at the moon (238,000 miles); in thirty-four hours, having travelled 45 million miles, you could be shooting past Mars. At the end of the first week in space the milometer will have clocked up 1100 million miles. In twelve days, instead of twelve years, you will reach Neptune. After one year of continuous travel you will be approaching the speed of light (186,300 miles per second). However, by then you will have travelled so far into space that your speed relative to the earth will have no meaning. The sun will have become a distant star of red appearance and your concern will then be whether Einstein's theory really does act as a barrier on your speed. According to him nothing can exceed the speed of light because the greater the speed, the greater the force needed to increase speed. Even an infinite force could be insufficient to penetrate the ceiling set by the speed of light.

Despite such limitations, speed is obviously of the essence in getting to your chosen destination in space as quickly as possible. The faster you cover the vast distances involved, the fewer provisions you have to carry and the less demand you have on life support systems such as oxygen. Going to Mars on a packed lunch is a much more attractive prospect than having to take along enough food to last you a year!

But there is an even more important reason for calculating our travel at the acceleration of One G. By doing so you will recreate earth's gravity within the spacecraft. This means that passengers will only be subjected to normal body pressures and will suffer no weightlessness. You will have taken a bit of the earth's environment with you as you streak across the heavens. There will be none of the physical side-effects or psychological disorders arising from prolonged exposure to non-gravity conditions.

What we are really talking about here is future travel in something similar to what many people describe as 'flying saucers'. I don't necessarily believe what others say about these phenomena but I keep an open mind on their possibility. After all, millions of people have sworn they have spotted these unidentified flying objects since the dawn of civilization. Many even claim to have seen and spoken to their passengers. Dismiss these eye witness accounts as you will. But one thing cannot be denied. If flying saucers do exist they are capable of travelling vast distances at 'impossible' speeds in contradiction of our physical laws here on Earth.

Building such a machine is what we must aim for. It is the only way of crossing our final frontier.

Chapter 2

Before I tell you about myself let me tell you about my father. He was an outstanding engineer, one of the natural variety who had a wonderful pair of hands and a highly innovative mind. He had nothing in principle against engineers who had university or college qualifications. But he had little time for those academic types who swanked about with fancy degrees and were scared of getting their hands dirty. He called them 'pretend engineers' taking the easy way out.

His definition of a real engineer was someone who had all the practical skills necessary to make things. They had to be able to design the product, manufacture and assemble it, then finally get it to work. What you read out of text books was all very well, according to him, but it was what you accomplished on the shop floor that really made you an engineer.

All his life he practised what he preached. He could, make virtually anything he turned his mind to, from watches, cameras, and engine components, right down to hedge-cutters and a wide range of tools for his own workshop. I remember him turning out cigarette lighters so small you could get three of them on an old silver threepenny piece. He even made some of our shoes and clothes. But it was in his job as a foreman engineer with food processing firms in Edinburgh, and later Dundee, that his inventive mind really got to work. He was constantly devising improvements in production techniques, particularly in conveyancing and handling systems. One of his brainchilds was an electronic monitoring system for controlling the butter-fat content of milk before it reached the boiling stage.

Although all these innovations saved his employers a fortune he made nothing out of it himself. His real reward came from pitting his ingenuity against intractable problems. He wouldn't even think of calling himself an inventor. To him that would have been pretentious and arrogant and that simply wasn't Matthew Kidd's style. He was

5

a modest, retiring man who never got his name up in lights, but to me he was always exceptional, an ideal.

The skills I have today were inherited from him and then developed under his influence. He taught me how to turn on a lathe and handle all the other tools you require for working in wood and metal. He drummed into me his philosophy of engineering: '*Make things, and make them work.*' He said it almost every day. I have never forgotten these words. All my life I have striven to uphold his standards.

Even as a toddler in Edinburgh, where I was born in 1937, I was always using my hands. In fact, before I went to primary school I simply assumed that everybody made something and everyone was an engineer. My brother Tom, now a consultant development engineer, was encouraged in exactly the same way. I can remember my poor mother, still alive today but now a widow, being driven mad by the three of us turning the house into a workshop; father in the kitchen, Tom in the living room, and me in the bedroom upstairs. What a din!

We also spent a lot of time round the meal table discussing possible inventions. One day my father produced a magazine article which said that the person who could design a successful pea de-podder would become a millionaire. It was a challenge we couldn't resist. For months everything else was pushed aside while we concentrated all our efforts in trying to crack this particular problem, egging each other on with talk of a new life in the Bahamas. But finally we had to give up when the pea season ended and we ran out of our raw material.

By then, however, I had been well and truly bitten by the inventive bug, to such an extent that when my pals were out playing football or at the cinema I would be sitting at home with a furrowed brow trying like fury to think up something new. I was only sixteen when I designed my own two-stroke engine, one that would eliminate the problem of getting residual exhaust gas out of the combustion chamber in time for the new charge coming in. I burned the midnight oil for months over that somewhat ambitious project. Ten years later I successfully built the engine, but shortly after my interest switched to something else and I did nothing more with it.

A push-bike which could give a full range of speeds with only half the pedal power was another of my bright ideas. It was built on the principle of the pedals going up and down instead of the usual circular motion. However, it involved mechanical linkages and cranks and my father reckoned it would have been uneconomic for mass production. But I'm definitely having one for my old age!

Aeroplanes became my special interest from an early age. This had a lot to do with the war. I was only two when it began and everyone was talking about air raids and building shelters to protect ourselves from enemy bombs. Needless to say, my father built us a posh underground bunker, a real five-star affair, on the small garden plot attached to our council house at Carricknowe in the Corstorphine area of Edinburgh.

During the war years I followed the exploits of the RAF as closely as a plotter in an operational control room. I wouldn't leave home for school each day until I heard the latest news on the wireless about our gains and losses in the aerial battles. My heroes were the men who flew the fighters and the bombers, the Spitfires and the Lancasters, and all the other British aircraft which were writing such a glorious chapter in the history of aerial combat.

It was only natural, therefore, that I started to make my own model aeroplanes. First the big ones in kit form complete with construction drawings. These flew by 'rubber power', lengths of elastic running through the fuselage from the tailpiece to the propeller which you wound up, then released to provide the energy for take-off. But it was the smaller, radio-controlled aircraft that really caught my imagination when I was much older and to this day I still fly these models, attending rallies all over the country whenever I can.

Soon, however, as a youngster, I was looking beyond aeroplanes. By the time I was eight I was hooked on spacecraft and the mysteries of the universe and from that age began reading endlessly about astronomy and the evolution of man. That in turn took me into science fiction which whetted my appetite for space exploration. I remember building a kite and buying all the balls of string I could afford out of my pocket money until, when I launched it, this make-believe space ship of mine became a speck in the sky. It flew so high, in fact, that one day the local bobby came to the house and told me I would have to lower my altitude because the kite was a possible hazard to aircraft coming in to land at Edinburgh Airport. I remember telling the policeman I was trying to reach the moon. He just laughed and rumpled my hair.

We left our native city in 1951 and headed north to Dundee where my father had landed a better job with a big milk supply company. It was there, at Grove Academy in Broughty Ferry, that

I received most of my secondary education. I wanted to enrol in the technical grade but the rector insisted that my previous school reports merited me a place in the top academic stream and that's where I landed. I enjoyed the science and the chemistry classes but the poetry and the Latin left me cold. I neither wanted to be another Keats nor become a pharmacist. I simply wanted to be an engineer like my Dad.

In those days a high premium was placed on skills within working-class families like my own. An apprenticeship was the gateway to a solid future on a livable wage. It was no surprise, therefore, when I left school at sixteen. I'm sure that if I had wanted to stay on, then go to university and become something like a brain surgeon, my father, with a twinkle in his eye, would have said: 'Aye laddie, that's fine. But first I think you should learn a skill.'

At that time, in 1953, Dundee still boasted a wide range of heavy industry with plenty of openings for young school leavers like me. I had no difficulty in landing a five-year apprenticeship as a fitter-toolmaker with a textile machine manufacturer. During the first year I started attending engineering classes one day a week at the local technical college for my ordinary national certificate in mechanical engineering. The course lasted three years and was the time-honoured way of combining work practice with classroom theory.

Despite achieving excellent results I threw in the towel during the second year. It wasn't that I didn't want to study because I was lazy, but, as with school, I found so much of what I was being taught totally irrelevant to my needs. I wasn't really interested in stuffy old theories. I wanted to find out about all the latest developments in gas turbines, rocket motors and airframes – information I was able to devour from magazines and journals. At other times I simply wanted to make things. It was this practical approach to knowledge that was to stand me in such good stead later on. Indeed, if I had believed what the textbooks said about the impossibility of anti-gravity machines I would never have tackled such a project in the first place.

Despite quitting my studies I didn't lose my job. In fact, several months later, the boss called me into his office and said: 'Sandy, I want you to come into the drawing office and train as a draughtsman. You have more aptitude than anyone else in this place and I want to put that to good use.' I thanked him but said no thank you. I just wanted to make things like my Dad.

When my apprenticeship was finished I got married to a

local girl, Janet Nicoll, then went off to start my National Service. I had no difficulty in choosing the uniform. It was the royal blue of the Air Force. I reported to Bridgenorth for 'square bashing' and was later posted to the famous Dambusters' base at Scampton in Lincolnshire where I began as a technician in 83 Squadron working on Vulcan bombers. Shortly afterwards, when Janet became pregnant, the strain of separation proved too much so I took the Queen's shilling for nine years. This gave me married quarters and the unaccustomed wealth of £12 a week.

Life at Scampton went along happily enough and I earned a promotion, becoming an air radar mechanic with the rank of senior aircraftsman. But after five years' service we were struck by tragedy. Sandra, our only child at that time, became ill with cancer of the lymph glands. She had no chance and we were warned to expect the worst. Over the next twelve months, despite everything the doctors could do, we had to stand by helplessly and watch our beloved daughter being slowly taken from us. Although she wasn't quite five years old she seemed to understand she was going off somewhere else. We promised her that some day we would all meet up again in heaven. I can't possibly describe our feelings at that time. You have to suffer the heartbreak yourself to understand what it does to you. But I can tell you this – that experience strengthened the bond between Janet and me and fortified us to withstand the tremendous pressures on our marriage which were to come later on.

Having lost Sandra I was granted a compassionate discharge from the RAF and we returned to Dundee where I took up my former trade as a toolmaker. At the age of thirty I became one of the youngest toolroom foremen in the country with forty men under my wing. My father was the proudest man in Britain. Toolmakers were the elite of the engineering industry. They had all the basic skills and could therefore go on to become anything in the manufacturing field. They also needed nerves of steel. If you were given a production machine to modify and made a mistake in carrying out the specification it could mean a fortune thrown away. If you were asked to grind something to one-ten-thousandth of an inch you were expected to get it spot-on. As a foreman I carried the can for getting everything right.

Building on my experience I moved around, first to become a process and development engineer and then, in quick succession, an electrical draughtsman and an instrument planning engineer. Later I became an electrical design supervisor responsible for surveying the complete electrical installations of Shell's oil production platform in the North Sea.

But it was on the shop floor that I really became an engineer. That was the campus I graduated from. It was there also that I learned how to argue my case in the fierce, endless discussions we had on topical issues of the day. Shop floors were the debating chambers out of which some of Britain's leading politicians and trade union leaders emerged to make their mark on the national scene. I regret none of this. I like to think I took honours in the hardest university of them all. I didn't get letters after my name, but I made things.

Looking back on it all now, I think that various disconnected episodes in my life were somehow preordained, almost like a preparation for some great task ahead. I know other people have said this about themselves when about to embark on some daunting project. But I really believe this to have been true about myself. There was the influence of my father which led me to become an engineer and an innovator; my obsession with the mysteries of the universe; an incident in the RAF which I will tell you about shortly; the new perspective on life I gained from the death of my daughter, one which gave me the determination to use what time I still had left to fulfil my ambitions.

All these separate elements were to be drawn together into a unified force when the time came.

Chapter 3

It had seemed like just another routine day when I set out early from home in the village of Dunholm on that August morning in 1962 to report for duty at RAF Scampton. As I pedalled my push-bike leisurely along the backroads of Lincolnshire my thoughts were already on the Vulcan bombers of 83 Squadron waiting for their pre-flight checks at the airfield five miles further on. It was then seven o'clock. By nine they would start taking off, roaring across rural England on a training flight that could take them to any part of the country.

By mid-afternoon they would begin dropping gently back out of the sky, coming into land at regular intervals and taxiing to the dispersal areas just off the perimeter track. The crews would then be debriefed with technicians like myself from the various trades standing by to rectify reported faults.

The Vulcan was an impressive aeroplane, covered overall in a pure white anti-radiation paint to reflect the heat of exploding nuclear bombs. With one and a half acres of wing surface alone she was built like a battleship but could soar like a bird at great heights, across enormous distances at over 600 mph. The Vulcan dropped her first bombs in anger during the Falklands War, right at the end of her active service.

I had been thrilled when my posting came through to Scampton, the base made famous through its Dambuster connection during the Second World War. It was from there that the Lancasters launched their epic raid over Germany in 1943, breaching the Ruhr dams with the ingenious bouncing bombs invented by Barnes Wallis. I was only six years old at the time but vividly remember hearing all about the daring exploit led by Guy Gibson, later decorated with the Victoria Cross. Whenever we were discussing the subject of boffins at home the name of the remarkable Wallis, an outstanding aeronautical engineer, was sure to crop up. Now I was actually serving on the base which had been at the centre of that thrilling operation.

By three o'clock that afternoon the Vulcans started coming into roost, their airframes shimmering in the heat of a scorching summer's day. Within ten minutes of landing the debriefing session was in full swing. One of the navigators reported a stabilization fault in the scanner of his aircraft and the chief technician told me to remove its gyro mechanism and replace it with another unit.

The scanner is a long, rectangular aluminium structure which is curved along its length. It rotates all the time to give a continuous picture of the ground around the aircraft while it is in flight. This picture is used for navigation purposes and pinpointing bombing targets. It is imperative that the scanner always remains parallel to the ground to maintain the accuracy of the picture, despite all the manoeuvring of the aircraft. This stability is achieved by the use of a gyroscope which, when rotating at high speed, has the ability to remain in the same position indefinitely if allowed to do so. This is why gyros are used in ships' compasses and the advanced stabilization systems of modern liners. They are in fact a point of reference when everything around them is constantly moving.

The gyro is normally no more than a metal wheel rotating on a shaft. The toy models have always been very popular with youngsters because gyros appear to react unpredictably when forces are applied to them in certain ways. They seem to have minds of their own. Under certain circumstances their actions are still not properly understood by experts. But one thing is well established. They build up fantastic energy during rotation and will use that energy to react violently to any force that disturbs them. For that reason proper gyros can be very dangerous things to play about with.

To remove the gyro mechanism from the scanner meant crawling under the cockpit to gain access to the nose of the aircraft through a bulkhead door. The gyro was contained in a small, domed aluminium box weighing about three pounds. Clutching the box to my chest with one hand, I used the other to grope backwards through the confined space and then down the steep ladder at the side of the bomber.

When I reached the ground I turned sharply to walk across the apron. Suddenly, without warning, I was knocked clean off my feet, falling heavily on my back and jarring every bone in my body. I felt as if I had been hit with a sledgehammer, although there was no one near me. For several seconds I lay badly dazed, looking up at the sky and trying to sort out my confused thoughts. Then it dawned on me. Although the gyro had been turned off after the Vulcan landed, it still had ample energy in the system to keep it spinning at high speed in its box. I had overlooked that possibility and by turning sharply at the foot of the ladder had disturbed the gyro from its path of rotation. Characteristically it had objected with a violent kick and it was that invisible blow which had knocked me over.

In the weeks following that alarming event I could think of nothing else but the sheer power contained within that spinning wheel. I reached the conclusion that a gyro was simply a battery of energy which could be tapped if you knew how to do it. This simple mechanical device was capable of producing several hundred times its own weight in energy output. Such a device, I thought, could be the answer in developing a revolutionary propulsion system, one in which a number of gyros grouped together in a spacecraft would give you the power to travel between galaxies. These were the exciting thoughts that filled my mind during the remainder of my service at Scampton. It was the first time I had ever considered the prospect of an anti-gravity machine. The seed had now been sown in my mind.

After returning to 'civvy street' in 1964 I became preoccupied with bringing up two young daughters and establishing myself back at work as an engineer. But during these busy years I still found time to carry out simple gyro experiments, observing their antics and trying to reach a better understanding of how they behaved. The more I got to know them the more intrigued I became. They were totally different from any other engineering mechanism I had come across. Once you spun them up they would rotate for ages under their own momentum and, through that very spinning motion, would become a closed energy system. This is not the same as a perpetual motion machine which endeavours to give you something for nothing but has never yet been proved feasible and, in my view, never will. With gyros you have to put energy in to get them going before you can get energy back out. They will give no more out than you put in. But they have this tremendous ability to store energy under rotation. They simply bank it. All this observational knowledge was carefully filed away in my mind for use at some future time. Its application in a space-drive situation continued to lurk in my thoughts. But I needed something to galvanize me into action, another incident like the Vulcan bomber gyro which would finally commit me to building some sort of prototype machine.

The catalyst arrived at the end of 1974 with two separate events but involving the same person: Professor Eric Laithwaite,

Emeritus Professor of Heavy Electrical Engineering at Imperial College, London, and one of the world's most distinguished experts in his field. He was celebrated for his development of the linear induction motor which, together with his other work in electromagnetic levitation, had led to the concept of transport without wheels and, in particular, the high-speed linear train.

On November 8 that year the professor carried out an extraordinary demonstration during a lecture at the Royal Institution in Albemarle Street, London. The Royal Institution is a highly prestigious body open to everyone interested in science and technology. It has always been actively engaged in research and, since being founded in 1799, many of the world's most momentous scientific advances have been made within its walls, none more notable than Michael Faraday's discovery of electromagnetic induction which paved the way for today's electrical industries. The Institution also provides a forum where members can hear experts speak about their subjects and describe their latest discoveries. This is partly done through what are called Friday Evening Discourses and it was at one of these that Professor Laithwaite caused a sensation in scientific circles. The Discourses are very formal affairs and involve a certain ritual. They attract an audience of around four hundred and fifty with the majority, including the technician assisting the speaker, wearing dinner jackets. The speaker is escorted through the building to the lecture theatre by the director in case, it is facetiously suggested, he tries to escape. On the stroke of nine, two hall porters solemnly swing open the door of the theatre and the speaker makes his entrance, almost like a gladiator stepping into the ring of the Colosseum. It is all very awe-inspiring.

What the professor did that evening was to demonstrate a gyroscopic machine which he claimed produced vertical lift without any external reaction. He did this by placing the device on an ordinary set of kitchen spring balance scales, setting the gyros in motion, then announcing that the weight of the machine was being reduced from twenty pounds to about fifteen pounds as the spinning wheels used their rotational energy to oppose gravity.

The demonstration had been previewed in that day's edition of the *Daily Express* by science writer Chapman Pincher. He revealed that the world's first anti-gravity machine to defy Newton's laws would be unveiled that evening before leading scientists at the Royal Institution. Professor Laithwaite was quoted: 'This must

14

be the breakthrough for which all my work has so far been a preparation. This machine, and the bigger ones we shall build, do not disprove Newton's Laws of Motion but show that they need modification. The achievement of weight reduction by a system of gyroscopes means that the jets used to move spaceships once they are in orbit can be replaced. Since jets are useless when they run out of fuel, space travel has so far been limited to the planets. With gyros operated by nuclear energy it will be possible to explore other solar systems. There may also be immediate application to boats, providing silent propulsion.'

After the event the popular press seized on the story and wrote it up for days under eye-catching headlines – 'The Machine That Can Defy Gravity' . . . 'They're Up In the Air Over the Professor's Gravity Buster' . . . 'Eric Laithwaite Defies Newton'. An official of the Royal Institution was quoted as saying the demonstration had proved Einstein and Newton were both wrong and that such a device used in space travel would reach two-thirds of the speed of light within weeks. He believed its commercial applications could be mammoth, 'possibly equal to fifty or sixty North Sea oil fields.'

But another newspaper reported that the professor's colleagues at Imperial College were giving his claims a cool response. One of the top academics was quoted: 'It is such very thin ice to skate on that I'm not going to stick my neck out.' A writer in the *New Scientist* was of the opinion that the professor had not proved his case. More precise experiments, he said, were necessary. According to one report the professor responded to the criticism by stating: 'I think you could say that some of my colleagues – better known for their ability to criticize than for their constructive attitude – left a little disappointed that my machine worked.' The professor had certainly stirred up a hornet's nest, to such an extent that his paper delivered that night, 'All Things Are Possible', was rejected for publication on scientific grounds.

The second event that finally clinched my commitment came shortly after during another Royal Institution tradition, their annual Christmas lecture series, by then being televised and that year being delivered by the same Professor Laithwaite. In one of these popular science programmes the professor carried out a fascinating experiment, with a young boy tied to a pole on a turntable being handed a three-foot shaft at the end of which was a forty-five-pound spinning gyroscope. When the turntable was accelerated the wheel soared into the air as easily as if the boy was opening an umbrella. When the turntable was decelerated the gyro dipped towards the ground. But in whichever direction the gyro moved the remarkable thing was the boy could easily support it. The gyro was actually using its rotational energy to fly.

I was now convinced I had all the evidence necessary to support my belief that the answer to space travel and exploration lay in the mysterious properties of the gyroscope. Such a device, properly developed, could also be used to give us the flying motor car, ships that speed through water without thrashing propellers, and aeroplanes which would cover the 12,000 miles from London to Sydney in about twenty minutes. There would be no need to emigrate. You would simply fly home after finishing work on a Friday in whichever part of the world you happened to be and then fly back again on the Monday morning.

I therefore took the irrevocable decision to build an anti-gravity machine or, to give it a more scientific description, an inertial drive device or a prime mover. There was no bravado in this determination. I didn't see it in terms of Sandy Kidd taking on the world single-handed. This was a very personal commitment, like someone being called to the church or to medicine. Everything within me dictated that I should do this. My decision was deeply instinctive. I had seen the scorn poured on Professor Laithwaite over his efforts but this did not deter me in the slightest. The challenge that faced me was not only building a gyroscopic machine that would produce thrust, but one which would also provide sufficient evidence to make it acceptable to the scientific fraternity. This was going to be the most difficult task of all; getting people to believe in it. By its very definition anti-gravity stands for contravention of the established laws of physics. The plain truth of the matter is that you simply cannot open up the universe in any meaningful way and at the same time conform to textbook physics. If you achieve the first you automatically change the second.

If gyroscopes had belonged to some other branch of engineering, say electronics, I would never have tackled this mission. But spinning wheels are a mechanical phenomenon. This was meat and drink to a toolmaker. Whatever machine had to be built I could design it, make and assemble all the components, and then hopefully make the whole thing work.

'*Make things, and make them work.*' That's what my father always said.

Chapter 4

Big personal decisions inevitably lead to an upheaval in life style. I knew by the very nature of what I was tackling that our normal family existence would have to be radically altered. If I had been able to give up my job and concentrate full time on designing and building this machine I could have retained some semblance of family life. But with a wife and two young daughters to support I obviously had to carry on earning my livelihood while at the same time increasingly devote all my spare time to the project. The situation would be equivalent to having two jobs, but being paid for only one.

By now, of course, Janet and the two girls were accustomed to having me about the house participating in everything a father is expected to take part in: shopping, gardening, decorating, chauffeuring, homework, and the multitude of other commitments which you gladly shoulder as a parent. You can only abdicate these responsibilities and keep the marriage intact if you have a wife who has total sympathy with your cause and is willing to adopt the role of widow, conducting day-to-day affairs more or less single-handed. Fortunately Janet was such a wife. She was already fond of describing me affectionately to others as 'never having been quite normal', in the sense that from the very first days of going out together she had appreciated my preoccupation with anything to do with the mysteries of the universe. She was also aware of my appetite for reading and during our courting years had spent hours with me in the local library while I poured over all the latest scientific and engineering developments in the magazines and journals I couldn't afford to buy. Occasionally she would complain about never getting to the cinema like other couples or having the opportunity of wearing her dancing shoes. But to tell the truth, I was much more interested in Einstein and Newton than I ever was in Clark Gable or Spencer Tracy or, for that matter, waltzing and fox-trotting at the local palais. But now that I had taken the big decision to go it alone

Janet readily accepted her fate, not in any grudging way, but with a deep understanding of the inner compulsion which was driving me on. I shall never forget her words at the time: 'Right, you go for the stars and I'll look after things down here.'

There were, of course, other adjustments to be made as well. Our social life with family and friends would have to be severely curtailed. No longer would I be able to spend hours every week helping colleagues to tune their car engines for hill climbs and cross-country events. I had also become the local Mr Fixit. Any of our friends and neighbours whose household gadgets needed repairing could always depend on Sandy doing the necessary. That, too, would have to stop.

What Janet and I actually did I suppose was to draw up an emergency plan of action, in much the same way as we would have done had I been going off to work somewhere abroad where I couldn't take my family. The only difference was that I was still going to be at home but with a 'Don't disturb' notice hanging permanently round my neck.

All this readjustment took effect gradually, so that no one else was aware for a long time that something was going on in the Kidd household. The last thing I wanted was to announce my intentions with a fanfare of trumpets. Those closest to us eventually realized I was working on some kind of revolutionary device. But for obvious reasons I didn't want the whole world to believe that a freak called Sandy Kidd was attempting to build a flying saucer. That's how stories get out of hand if you shoot your mouth off indiscreetly. In any case, at this early stage I had no idea what sort of machine I was going to build or, more importantly, whether it would ever be successful. Only one thing was certain. The main ingredient of the device would be the gyroscope.

I soon discovered there was little I could study on the subject that was really going to be helpful. Certainly no book had ever been written on how to build an anti-gravity device using spinning wheels. There was plenty of algebra available about gyroscopic behaviour but no satisfactory explanation whatsoever on how gyros behaved as a means of propulsion.

Other people, of course, had already taken out patents on inertial drive devices involving gyroscopes but as far as I could discover none had been developed and, indeed, many were simply 'paper machines' – all theory and no physical substance. The space drive I had read a bit about was the one invented by an American, the late Norman

Dean. Not many people saw it work because seemingly he wanted a Nobel Prize and a lot of bucks up front before he would even take it out of its box. But according to reports the Dean Machine jumped up and down on bathroom scales and showed loss of weight. At the end of the day, however, it disappeared into the mythology that has grown up round a subject which is often regarded as being akin to black magic.

Even the best of the science fiction writers, whose stories were often so prophetic, had never to my knowledge – and I was a prolific reader of their work – mentioned the use of gyroscopes in space drives as a means of powering star ships. These writers had plenty to offer in their stories about the shape of spacecraft, but not their propulsion. Ironically, however, shape was comparatively unimportant to me at this stage. You could send a scaffold through space if you had the means. Aeroplanes, on the other hand, depend on their configuration for much of their efficiency. They are aerodynamic vehicles and therefore shape is of the essence.

But none of these considerations applied to an anti-gravity machine. What I could have done with, though, was the invention of Mr Cavor, the central character in the H.G. Wells' novel, *The First Man in the Moon*, written in 1901. Mr Cavor created a magical substance called Cavorite which could insulate bodies from the force of gravity. Now that would really have been a boon to me!

As things were, however, I had to start from virtually nothing. There was no existing technology to build upon, as there had been when I developed my two-stroke engine and labour-saving bicycle. This was venturing into the largely unknown. I would be like an explorer, proceeding by stealth and testing the ground with every step in the knowledge that no one had ever succeeded in climbing this particular mountain before and sticking a flag in at the top which announced the arrival of anti-gravity.

* * * * *

From the time I got down to serious business in 1975, it took me several years to finally decide on the basic features of the machine I wanted to build. This was a period of trial and error during which I carried out a comprehensive programme of gyro experiments, much more advanced than the familiarity tests I had conducted earlier.

In those days I had no workshop, so I started by building a small test rig in my kitchen. It consisted merely of a metal base

19

which was free to swivel at the slightest movement and was capable of taking various combinations of gyros. First I mounted a single gyro, then a pair and finally a set of three. The wheels were spun up with a belt drive from an electric drill and put through endless trials involving different gyro sizes, weights and rotational speeds. I kept varying the length of the gyro rods and the angles at which they were set to their mounting or fulcrum. In the case of two or three gyros running simultaneously, a careful note was taken of how they reacted to one another, rather like observing the behaviour of twins and triplets.

Having exhausted all these permutations I repeated the tests all over again, but this time introducing the factor of forced precession. Precession is simply the term used to describe the drifting movement of a spinning gyroscope, the path it takes under its own steam. Whereas before my gyros had been precessing at their own volition, I now began to force them round as well, in a swinging circular movement, by rotating their swivel base with a turning handle. This meant I was applying rotary acceleration to the spinning gyros, which in turn was creating what is known as centrifugal force. You can produce exactly the same effect by swinging a brick on the end of a piece of string round and round your head. Although you can feel the brick building up considerable rotational energy through this movement, it will never rise above the horizontal because it is a dead weight unable to overcome the downward pull of gravity. But the unique properties of a gyro in the same situation will cause it to rise up despite its weight, as I had witnessed during Professor Laithwaite's television demonstration with the young boy on the turntable. The gyro, I now discovered for myself, was capable of using its accumulated energy to react against the centrifugal force by taking the path of least resistance, which was to move upwards. It was my belief and hope that when the gyros rose vertically in whatever device I eventually built they would take the machine with them under the power of their own thrust. But even if the lift only amounted to several ounces, I was convinced that this alone would constitute a tremendous scientific achievement.

Throughout this period I carefully studied helicopter technology and was encouraged to find that it contained a good deal of gyroscopic theory. Although the helicopter is basically an aerodynamic craft it depends very largely on the effects of the centrifugal force created by its rotor blades to keep it airborne. Helicopter rotor blades are very flexible when static but under rotation become rigid due to the

20

centrifugal effect and it is this 'strengthening' of the blades which keeps the helicopter aloft.

By 1978, therefore, from the mass of data I had compiled, I knew that my machine would have a balanced system of two gyros, each one rotating at the end of a crossarm attached to a vertical shaft which would be spinning round at the same time. It would be a forced precession device with a continuous source of power being fed to the gryos and the main rotating shaft.

Having decided on the basic concept of the machine I was now able to shut down my test rig in the kitchen, much to Janet's relief. She had soldiered on bravely, making and serving the family meals in the midst of whirling gyroscopes, cans of lubricating oil and a battery of rather greasy tools which sometimes found their way into the cutlery drawer. They say that two women can never successfully share a kitchen. If nothing else I had already proved that a kitchen was not the ideal setting either for a small engineering workshop. But from my point of view the end had justified the means. Now I was in a position to move into a less congested area of the house with my drawing board and get down to more detailed planning for the day when I would actually start making all the components required for my machine.

Because my approach to this project had to be purely pragmatic, I realized that the device would undergo many changes in the light of all the hard, practical experience that lay ahead in the construction and testing periods. That, after all, is what a prototype is all about. By this time I had been a process and development engineer for eight years working on new machine tools, so I knew only too well that things seldom worked first time and if they did they could always be made to work better. Nevertheless you must have something to start with, and I now began to work out the other essential ingredients of my gyroscopic propulsion unit.

What I was aiming for in general terms was simplicity and reliability. With a machine that would be subjected to abnormal stresses and strains through its rotational movements and resultant vibration, it was essential I keep the design as simple as possible to facilitate and reduce maintenance and repair. Only by doing this would I ever achieve the second factor of reliability. It would be a complete waste of time ending up with a fancy device which promised much but delivered little because it kept breaking down. It had to be dependable. It also had to be as light in weight as possible. Anything too heavy, especially in the early stages, would obviously make it much more difficult to overcome the downward force of gravity. Aluminium alloy, therefore, would be the main metal I would use.

Slowly the overall design took shape out of literally hundreds of drawings and pages of calculations. I went through enough paperwork to plan a battleship. Even before I got down to work with paper and pencil, I had juggled things around in my head for months. But I now knew that my provisional machine would have a central vertical shaft of five inches with the crossarm drive to the gyro at either end being three feet in diameter. The gyros themselves would be of bronze, much heavier than aluminium, but because of that able to build up rotational energy at lower speeds and therefore reduce the element of fatigue. Each gyro would weigh one and a quarter pounds and have a diameter of three and a half inches. Although they would take their power through the horizontal crossarm each gyro would be mounted rigidly on to a support arm which would run down to the bottom end of the vertical shaft where it would be attached to the central column by a loose pin known as the fulcrum. These arms would consequently be able to swing up and down in whichever way the gyros wished to move in the vertical plane. The gyros would actually be held up at the correct angle by restraining links, each one running from the end of the crossarm up to the top of the vertical shaft. This framework would give the machine the overall shape of a diamond.

My next consideration was how the machine and the gyros should be powered. Here my decision was dictated by cost. It would have been ideal to have gone out and bought variable-speed electric motors and control units ready-made for the job. But these would have cost several hundred pounds and without the slightest guarantee that I was even going to succeed in building an anti-gravity machine, the last thing I wanted to be left with at the end of the day was a load of expensive equipment. Indeed, I was determined that my whole machine would be constructed on a shoestring budget. I therefore decided that an old vertical electric drill I already possessed would supply the power for rotating the entire machine. In other words, it would be the precession drive. The drill would be hitched up to the top of the main central shaft by a belt and pulley system. The gyros would be powered by an electric motor attached to the bottom of the main shaft. Although I said nothing to Janet at the time I intended to 'borrow' the motor out of her washing machine!

From the time I had evacuated the kitchen in 1978, it had

taken me over two years to finalize these aspects of my prototype machine. But during this period I had also been coping with a big change in my career as an engineer. With the booming North Sea oil industry offering good money for skilled work, I had decided to set myself up as a one-man company and work as a freelance. My first contract was to work as an electrical draughtsman on drawings for one of Shell's exploration and production platforms. This job meant travelling each day to Montrose, thirty miles from Dundee, with occasional spells off-shore. This change in my working practice left me with considerably less time to devote to my own project, although being self-employed certainly gave me more flexibility than I had ever enjoyed before. I could now pick and choose the work I wanted to do. The thought had not escaped me, however, that if I did somehow achieve the breakthrough with an anti-gravity machine I wouldn't really have to worry about the need to work again. But until that day dawned, if it ever did, earning a living to meet my family commitments would have to remain my number one priority. We couldn't eat on the heady atmosphere of trying to open up the universe.

By now I had acquired a garden shed at the rear of my bungalow. It was only six feet by five – hardly big enough in which to swing a cat. But this was going to be my engineering workshop for the foreseeable future. Into this cramped space I set up a lathe, a vertical drill, a tool-grinding machine, a disc grinder and a shaping machine. I lined the walls with racks to hold dozens of hand tools. I also had to lay in power and heating. Although I would make and assemble everything in the shed, the actual testing of the machine would be carried out in my lock-up garage. There, too, I had to install electricity.

By the end of January 1981, everything was all set. There was frost in the air and snow on the ground. Working at nights and weekends in a garden shed wasn't exactly the most exciting prospect in town. But I knew within myself that it was time to start building the most important machine of my life. As I said to Janet, I simply couldn't go to my grave not knowing whether the whole thing was possible or not.

Chapter 5

My first task was to build the gyroscopes themselves, the spinning wheels which held the secret to everything I wanted to accomplish. It seemed incredible to me that in an age when man had landed on the moon and invented such marvels as the telephone, television and computer, he had still not mastered a complete understanding of the way gyroscopes behaved in certain circumstances. After all, they were only rotating discs, like the wheels on anything you care to think of that runs along the ground. But when you suspend them in space and subject them to certain forces they seemed to be capable of doing all sorts of weird things.

Because the gyros were going to be the most difficult of all my components to make I decided that, although other parts of the machine would inevitably be chopped and changed, the bronze wheels should stick to their original specification of one and a quarter pounds in weight and three and a half inches in diameter. In effect everything else would be tailored to fit round them. I made the outside rims the heaviest part. This is a feature of all gyroscopes because the rim, being the fastest moving part, is where most of the energy is stored during rotation. Having made the gyros I then set about machining all the other many components: bushes, bearings, brackets, linkages, pulleys, discs, connecting rods, support arms, restraining links, driving sleeves, spindles, universal ball couplings, and gear box.

I laboured long and hard at my crude production line, turning out high precision work with only basic tools, in conditions which were so cramped they almost made me claustrophobic. It was a slow, painstaking business. The crafting of all these parts went on throughout 1981 and into the spring of the following year. By then my job had taken me even further away from home. I had landed a contract with Shell in Aberdeen as an electrical design draughtsman working on the construction drawings for another of their production platforms. Each day I was spending over three hours in my car covering the return journey of 130 miles. How I kept wishing all that time could have been spent on my own project. Eventually, however, I reached the stage when I was able to assemble the machine for the first time.

In doing this it was important that the machine and the gyros should rotate in the same direction relative to each other, remembering that the machine would be rotating in a vertical plane and the gyros in a horizontal plane. If both were going in different directions the gyros would react by going downwards, which was the very opposite to the direction I wished them to take. I chose to have everything travel in an anti-clockwise direction, that is anti-clockwise when viewing the machine from above and when looking at the gyros from the outside. If, however, you viewed the gyros side-on from the front of the machine, the rims would be seen to travel in opposite directions to each other. This had meant building a special split-drive to the gyros by making a circular gear box containing three bevelled gears and fitting it to the base of the machine.

With the first version of the machine now completed I was ready at last to begin running trials. This, I knew, was only the start of a long haul ahead. But I thought I had mentally prepared myself for the thousands of hours of plodding, routine work which would have to be clocked up before I would get anywhere near the stage of achieving 'take off', if ever at all.

Remember, the philosophy of my machine was to rotate the entire device at a speed which would produce a measure of centrifugal force, not so big that the spinning gyros would be unable to overcome it and rise upwards, but powerful enough to allow the gyros to utilize all their energy to torque, or twist, against the force and, by cancelling it out, continue vertically with a strong thrusting action.

To succeed in this ultimate aim required matching the speed of the machine to the speed of the gyros. This, in turn, meant having the gyro support arms set at precisely the right angle to the vertical shaft so that the gyros were sitting in the correct position. The diameter of the crossarm was also vital because that largely determined the level of centrifugal force.

During the next two and a half years I built twelve different versions of my machine as I worked my way through every possible permutation of all these factors, striving endlessly to find the combination of speeds, sizes and angles which would give me the magic brew to overcome gravity. This became the nightmare period of the whole project. I was now totally obsessed with finding the answers, an obsession which gradually made me oblivious to everything else that was happening around me. Janet and my two daughters, Debbie and Wendy, were vague figures moving around the house, running their own lives and making their own decisions as if I didn't exist. Friends and neighbours, not seeing me for months on end, became naturally curious. Janet had strict instructions to say nothing about a space-drive machine. As far as others were concerned I was working on a new type of model aeroplane engine. I became known as the 'nutty professor', the man who spent all his spare time locked up in his shed and garage.

When Debbie married and had our first grandchild, Nicola came to see us each week. After some time, she never went into the house but made a beeline for the shed instead where she hammered on the door shouting 'Grandad'. The little lass actually thought her grandfather lived in this small wooden hut. I almost did when I wasn't at my work in Aberdeen. Each day I left home at seven in the morning and didn't arrive back again until seven at night. I would then be in my shed or garage until two the following morning. At weekends I was closeted with my machine from breakfast-time until midnight. I was living totally in a world of my own. I had cut myself off from the reality of life itself.

Throughout this period Janet coped magnificently, even on those occasions when the only thing I wanted to do when I crawled into bed in the middle of the night was to talk about the state of my project. She simply turned her hand to all the chores about the house which I had previously looked after. Things like redecoration, gardening, repairing fuses, laying carpets and sorting leaking taps. She became quite proud of her do-it-yourself expertise. On summer evenings she walked our two Yorkshire terriers. On winter nights she knitted furiously for our growing band of grandchildren. But even Janet with her almost unlimited supply of patience reached the point on several occasions when, like me, she felt she could go on no longer. When that happened, and she threatened to pack her bags and leave, we simply sat down and had a quiet chat over a cup of tea.

On these crisis occasions we always frankly admitted that had we properly appreciated the sacrifices involved we would never have started the project in the first place. There were no recriminations, just regret. But we also kept reaching the same decision to carry on. To give up, we agreed, would be to squander all the sweat, toil and tears we had already invested in getting to that stage. We simply had to struggle on. Indeed, as time progressed and I fell more and more under the influence of what I was creating in my garden shed, my own career as an engineer began to take a back seat. I was increasingly taking unpaid time off, as well as refusing lucrative overtime, to devote even greater effort to my own project. During these years I also had opportunities of earning big money in Saudi Arabia, Norway and Libya. But to have gone abroad would have taken me away from my machine. It was frustrating enough having to spend the odd week or two off-shore. To go 'foreign' was out of the question. As any expert will tell you, once you launch a research and development programme you must maintain continuity of effort to achieve the greatest efficiency. Constantly closing down and starting up a project like mine would simply have destroyed the driving force I had built up within myself. Turning my back on better jobs, of course, meant I was forfeiting thousands of pounds a year. But nothing, absolutely nothing, could stop me now. I had passed the point of no return.

When you are working under constant pressure in solitary confinement over an indefinite period one of the personal problems you run up against is, not surprisingly, loneliness. Sheer, utter loneliness. It engulfs you like a thick cloud, cutting you off from sight and sound of other people. You are, in fact, becoming a recluse against all your natural tendencies. It is a form of starvation. I got to the stage when I was treating the machine almost as if it was human. It had become the only thing in my life. To relieve this frightening sense of isolation, my son-in-law volunteered to keep me company several evenings a week, particularly during some of the long, dismal winter nights and early mornings when the creeping coldness and pitch blackness seemed only to underline the enormity of the task I was embarked upon. The presence of another person, someone to chat to during those interminable weeks and months, helped me to maintain my mental equilibrium.

As far as the machine was concerned my biggest worry in the early stages of the running trials was trying to find an electric motor strong enough to handle the gyros. It wasn't simply a case of powering up the wheels to the required speeds. The motors I was using, of half and three-quarter horse power, were more than adequate for that purpose. The problem really lay in starting the gyros up while the machine itself was already rotating. This imposed such a high starting load on the motors that they constantly burned out. I was 'stealing' motors out of washing machines, lawn mowers, vacuum cleaners, any domestic gadget in fact that I could get my hands on. Janet nearly skinned me alive. When I explained my problem to her she asked me the obvious question: 'Why don't you start up the gyros before the machine and prevent the overloading?'

Well, it wasn't as simple as that. The most important element in this complicated equation of forces was the centrifugal force generated by the rotation of the machine. That had to be present before the gyros started spinning, otherwise the wheels would simply precess upwards without opposition. It was the struggle to overcome the centrifugal force that made the gyros develop the 'muscle' for the thrust that would create the lifting effect.

In the end I was forced to look for an alternative form of power for the gyros without my having to buy expensive equipment. Finally, I found the very thing. Years before I had bought a 6 ½ cc internal combustion engine for one of my model aeroplanes. Air-cooled and capable of delivering one and a quarter horse power at 16,000 rpm, it was ideal for driving the wheels. All I had to do was to make a centrifugal clutch to allow me to gradually feed in the power and avoid overloading. It was this clutch that allowed me to control the speed of the gyros and without it I could never have properly run in the machine.

The engine, which had a glow plug ignition, was fuelled with a mixture of methol alcohol, castor oil and nitro methane. This type of engine was easier to operate than any other but it was also messier and created more fumes. I nearly choked to death on several occasions in the garage. Have you ever tried breathing in castor oil? Ugh! There were times when I was actually staggering about in the driveway gasping for fresh air. At other times I couldn't see the machine for smoke.

One of the other dangers I faced was a gyro breaking free from its mounting during rotation and scything through the air. When that happens they are lethal. It occurred twice during my stay in the garage. Each time the spinning wheel careered past my face and crashed into the concrete wall, leaving a gouge mark to remind me of the injury it would have inflicted had it struck me on the head. Eventually I decided on a safety measure. Taking an old outside door from the house, I propped it up in front of the machine when it was running at high speeds and viewed the proceedings through the letter box. If a stranger had chanced to see me they would have called for the men in white coats.

But still the work went on, throughout 1983 and into 1984, week after week, month after month, changing this, changing that, trying this and trying that. I was amazed by my own stamina. Never a day off or a holiday in years. Rarely more than four hours' sleep at night. Yet I kept going, spurred on by the thought that the next alteration in the machine would give me the elusive combination. Time and again I had to admit defeat. But provided I found an alternative way of running the device I never became downhearted. Options provided me with the oxygen to carry on. I kept telling myself that the answer might lie just round the next corner.

There was certainly never any shortage of problems. If it wasn't one thing it was another. One that really bugged me for a long time was belts breaking on the drives to the machine and the gyros. The belts were made of rubber and I glued the ends together after cutting them to size. But the joints kept coming apart, usually at the crucial stage of a test run. I was nearly driven mad. Finally I found the answer in polyurethane belts with welded joints. They had greater elasticity and were far more dependable.

By January 1984, I realized that whatever vertical thrust my machine might be capable of generating there certainly wasn't anything of the order that would lift all seven pounds of its weight. I had to be able to ascertain whatever lifting force the machine was producing, even if it was only a few ounces. To do this I hit upon the idea of rigging up a counterweight system as a balance to the machine. This consisted of a piece of string tied to the top of the vertical shaft and fed by pulleys along an overhead beam in the garage until it dangled down not far from where the device stood on a workbench. To the end of the string I tied a chunk of cast iron, stuck on a magnet and then added a number of small spanners. Their total weight was exactly the same as the machine which meant, in a sense, that it now had zero weight. Any vertical thrust at all, however small, would now allow the machine to lift and if that happened I could, by removing the spanners one by one and thereby making the machine heavier by reducing the weight of the counterbalance, calculate pretty accurately how much thrust the device was delivering.

Throughout the summer of that year I could sense I was entering the final stages of my programme. There weren't many more options left open to me now. The machine's appearance had undergone a marked change over the two years I had been building one version after another. It still had the shape of a diamond, but a much taller and slimmer diamond than the one with which I had started out. The main vertical shaft had grown from five inches to eighteen while the crossarm had been reduced from an overall diameter of three feet to fifteen inches. The gyro support arms had been gradually lifted from the almost-horizontal to an angle of fifty-three degrees.

The machine now had a certain battered look about it. Extensions to the support arms and the vertical shaft had been riveted into place. Bits of plate had been stuck on here and there. The whole thing looked decidedly scruffy. As a toolmaker I wasn't proud of the machine's aesthetic appearance. On the other hand, it had been constructed under my 'make do' plan with bits of metal scavenged out of scrap merchants' yards at a total cost of under fifteen quid. Not exactly a major capital investment. However, as I kept reminding myself, it was the geometry of the machine that really counted, not how pretty it looked.

Although I was still far from sure that I was going to achieve any breakthrough, I knew I was heading in the right direction through this long, painful process of elimination. If this machine couldn't defy gravity then no other device I could build would be able to do it either. I was as convinced as ever that I had all the essential ingredients. It was getting the mix right that was giving me nightmares.

In October, I set about preparing the machine for its last set of changes, now mainly involving the speed ranges. I finally fixed on the machine's rotation at a constant 280 rpm and duly made the appropriate size of pulley for the vertical electric drill which would control the speed at that level. I was going to run the gyros somewhere between 4000 and 6000 rpm.

I told Janet it would all be over soon, one way or another. The moment of truth arrived at last on November 21, 1984. It was my 47th birthday. It was also the day my patched-up machine, built in a humble garden shed, went through the gravity barrier for the first time, pulling itself free of earth's magnet to rise into the air against the counterweight with a thrust of eight ounces. It was the day when I sensed that my life would never be quite the same again.

Chapter Six

It took several days for the full significance of my machine's performance to sink in properly. When, in a state of exhaustion, you finally succeed in achieving something generally regarded as being impossible the initial reaction is often overwhelming relief – as in my case – rather than uninhibited joy. Gradually that relief gave way to a feeling of excitement, but one subdued by more than a little apprehension. Although I was convinced I had created a new type of force which challenged some of the most sacred laws of physics I realized, by that very claim, I would be met by disbelief, suspicion, and even downright ridicule when trying to have my evidence accepted by the Establishment.

The treatment meted out to Professor Eric Laithwaite in similar circumstances ten years earlier was still fresh in my memory. But, in a sense, my position was even more vulnerable than his. He was a towering intellectual. I was a nobody; a non-academic, someone without a track record who had built a machine, not in a laboratory or a proper engineering workshop, but in a humble garden shed and was now saying that this device opened up a new scientific era. I could already hear the hounds baying for my blood.

My first priority, therefore, was to make certain I could refute accusations that my machine was only producing an intermittent, freak effect and was nothing more than a useless curiosity. I had to be able to guarantee that the device consistently produced vertical thrust and, if need be, prove it to the doubters. The only way I could do this, of course, was to run the machine so often that I had absolutely no doubt in my own mind about its integrity.

Over the following two weeks I subjected the device to a concentrated programme of proving trials which involved three hundred runs. Not only did each one prove positive, but I was actually able to increase the measurement of thrust from the original eight ounces to almost twice that amount. I discovered that ball joints on the crossarm which should have had a clearance had bound together due to the machine's overall movement and this had been restricting the upward path of the gyros. When I rectified that fault the improvement in performance was almost as electrifying as the original result. In addition I felt justified in adding a few more ounces to compensate for the considerable 'drag' inherent in a system which was not sophisticated enough to overcome such handicaps as friction of the bearings and the tugging effect of the counterweight. I also knew that by making the machine lighter, and I was certain I could lose several pounds by using different materials, the lift expressed as a percentage of the machine's weight would be even more impressive. Taking all these factors into consideration made me feel on top of the world, if not yet over the moon.

But where did I go now? It was all very well having a machine which did the unexpected. But unless I could get certain influential people to share my faith in the gospel of anti-gravity on the basis of what I had achieved, then I would get no funding for the considerable research and development required to make gyroscopic propulsion a reality instead of a dream.

If I failed in that mission my machine would gather dust in the attic, a fate which I suspected had befallen other similar inventions. I had no intention of that happening to mine. The more I thought about the problem the more I realized I needed someone who could 'open doors' and, at the right time, give me the publicity I might require to gain credibility. The person I decided to approach was Ron Thompson, a senior reporter with Grampian Television in Dundee who had been appearing on-screen in my living room for about twenty years. Because of that I felt I knew him personally although, in fact, the first time I spoke to him was when I phoned his home the week before Christmas 1984.

When I asked if I could come and speak to him about a machine I had developed he seemed reluctant to meet me. He said something about inventors rarely living up to their claims. We fenced for several minutes, he wanting to know what the machine was all about and I not being prepared to go into details on the telephone. Eventually, when he more or less demanded to know what made my machine different from any other I lost patience. I still don't know exactly what made me think of the phrase but almost before I knew what I was saying I had blurted out: 'My machine is going to change the world, that's what.' The way I said it must have either impressed him, or he thought I was a variety of crank who called for further investigation. Whichever it was, he agreed to a meeting.

We met the following evening at the Grampian studio in West Ferry, a residential suburb of Dundee only a short distance from where I lived. The studio, remotely-controlled from the company's main station sixty-five miles away in Aberdeen, was located inside a converted Victorian mansion house standing in its own grounds at the top of a tree-lined driveway. When Janet and I arrived a few minutes early the place was in darkness so we waited at the side of the building until hearing Thompson approach up the drive. As I stepped forward to introduce myself the television man froze in his tracks, startled by the sudden movement in the shadows.

'It's all right, Mr Thompson,' I assured him. 'It's only the man who wants to change the world.'

He gave a short laugh and took us into the reception lounge on the ground floor where he invited us to sit round a coffee table in the middle of the spacious open-plan area. The rest of the building was deserted by that time of night, giving the place a certain eeriness but at least reassuring me that other people wouldn't be listening to what I was saying.

After an exchange of pleasantries I lit a cigarette and started to explain what my machine was all about. Thompson interrupted to warn me that he was technically illiterate so I would have to keep things simple. My heart sank. Trying to describe what I had done without sounding like some sort of crank was going to be difficult enough. Now it was going to be almost impossible but I battled on bravely, supplementing my explanation with a few rough sketches. Only when I spoke about opening up the universe did his interest really quicken. When I cautiously referred to flying saucers he nearly took off. After almost two hours of listening and note-taking Thompson departed, thoroughly bemused but promising to consult a professor he knew at the local university. Had I hooked him? I wasn't sure.

The following day I suddenly became impatient to get a quick, expert reaction to my machine while waiting on Thompson to come back to me. I simply couldn't contain my exuberance any longer over what I had achieved. I was going about in a dream, rather like someone who thinks they've won the jackpot on the pools but still requires confirmation before ordering up the champagne. My thoughts were constantly with the machine. Could it be, I asked myself time and again, that this creation of mine would someday change the whole course of mankind? By now I badly needed some sort of reassurance. But who could I turn to? Then it struck me. The guru himself, of course, Professor Eric Laithwaite, whose television lecture ten years earlier had inspired me to build the machine in the first place. Other people might have been intimidated at the prospect of approaching such a prominent academic out of the blue, but having never been overawed by titles before a name or letters after one I didn't give it a second thought. I simply picked up the telephone and put through a call to his office at Imperial College, London.

I explained to the professor's secretary who I was, what I had done, and that I wished to seek her boss's opinion and advice. She explained that the professor would not be back at the college until the end of the following month, January, 1985, but she would pass my message on to him as soon as possible. It sounded like a polite brush-off. But the following day she was back. The professor would like me to phone him at his home on the south coast. A few minutes later I was speaking to Eric Laithwaite himself. He was extremely receptive and seemed impressed when I described the machine and the amount of lift it had generated. As soon as I told him the gyros were mounted on pivots with sliding joints and were free to continually shift their position he interrupted.

'Now that is very interesting,' he said crisply. 'That is what you call skewed axes and there is no theory to predict how gyros will behave in certain circumstances when they are offset in this way.'

We talked further but at no stage did he attempt to play down my results or dismiss them as irrelevant.

When I offered to lay on a demonstration for him at Imperial College, he readily accepted. We agreed it should be soon after his return to duty and I promised to contact him later to fix the actual date. The professor's undoubted interest in what I had told him was a tremendous boost to my confidence. Two days later I was further encouraged when Ron Thompson told me that Professor Brian Makin, head of the Department of Electrical Engineering and Electronics at Dundee University, was also willing to look at the machine. He would bring him to my garage on the afternoon of Christmas Eve.

On that very day, however, I ran into mechanical failure while running the machine in preparation for their visit and when they arrived I was in the embarrassing position of having to explain that I couldn't get the required power out of the gyro engine because the clutch had burned out.

'Sod's Law,' remarked the professor philosophically. 'Never works when you want it to. I know the feeling.'

Brian Makin lost no time, however, in examining the machine, circling the device like a wrestler keeping a wary eye on his opponent. Then he began to prod and probe the various parts of the mechanism. Like Professor Laithwaite, he seemed particularly interested in the gyros' freedom of movement and how the flexible crossarm was coupled loosely to the vertical shaft. By this stage I had decided to switch from an air-cooled to a water-cooled engine to drive the gyros as an extra safeguard against overheating. To accommodate this I had simply suspended a can of water from one of the roof beams and led a plastic tube into the cylinder-head of the engine, with a bucket underneath to gather the hot water as it came through the system. Between that arrangement on one side of the machine and the counterweight set-up with magnet and spanners on the other, I could understand the look of amazement on Ron Thompson's face. He clearly thought he was looking at some kind of shambles. Makin, however, being an engineer viewed it differently and could appreciate the practicality of the rig.

Although I couldn't produce the revs needed to get the gyros lifting because of the faulty clutch, I ran the machine the best way I could to give my visitors some idea of how it looked in motion. I cringed a little when Thompson said the soft humming noise of the device rotating on its own reminded him of the description given by UFO observers to the sound they reported coming from flying saucers. Makin said nothing. He was deep in thought as we walked back into the house.

'So you think you've got something here?' he said at last in his Yorkshire accent, settling down in the lounge.

I braced myself for my first face-to-face encounter with the academic establishment. I had said nothing to Laithwaite about breaking any physical laws, but now I laid it on the line as I told Professor Makin quite bluntly that my machine was obviously creating a thrust without the need to react on air, water, or solid surface.

'You know what you're saying presumably?' he asked, sounding rather like a policeman warning that anything you say will be taken down and used in evidence against you. I nodded vigorously and decided to take the bull by the horns.

'Oh yes, I know the significance of my statement all right. But I'm afraid the academics will have to take another look at their textbooks. Because Sir Isaac Newton said three hundred years ago that every force applied must have an equal and opposite reaction doesn't mean to say we still have to swallow that dogma today. Let's face it, Newton didn't have the possibility of force-precessed gyros in mind when he drafted his Laws of Motion.'

Makin made it clear that my views would not be received too kindly. I told him, however, that after four years toiling in a garden shed there was no way I was going to have my machine dismissed by textbook theory. He made the point that evidence produced in a garage would require thorough verification in a more reliable environment before it could be properly assessed.

'This is a long drawn-out process,' he warned me. 'It means eliminating all other possible reasons for the machine's behaviour, such as vibrationary forces caused by the moving parts of the machine itself. What we call secondary effect.'

That, of course, was an argument I quite accepted. But, as I reminded him, if I produced a machine that appeared to do the 'impossible' it was up to the experts like himself to prove I was wrong. They simply couldn't walk away from such a device and pretend it didn't exist.

For some time we continued sparring with one another before parting amicably. He said he would be pleased to return when the machine was repaired and assess it for himself.

Several days later Ron Thompson told me he was going to follow the story through and would help me in any way he could. 'I've been waiting on a yarn like this in my thirty-four years as a reporter,' he told me. 'I don't know how it's going to end but if you're to be the man who is going to change the world, then I certainly want to be the man who is going to tell the world about it.'

As 1984 came to a close and the Kidd family quickly, and thankfully, settled back into a normal way of life, I looked ahead to the future with the same sense of wonder as a climber viewing Everest for the first time from Katmandu. Would I make it?

★ ★ ★ ★ ★

My main concern now was to prepare the machine for its demonstration at Imperial College in London. I had been told that others before me had beaten a path to the professor's door with a variety of inertial drive machines. Over the years he had seemingly become a father figure in such matters, a sounding board for the hopes and aspirations of inventors like myself.

The professor's position in all this really fascinated me. He

36

was first and foremost an international authority in electrical engineering, having developed the linear induction motor into an invaluable industrial tool. Over two hundred and eighty of his papers and articles had been published in learned society proceedings and technical journals. He had written sixteen books, fronted countless television series, and was a member of many eminent bodies. In his field he was unassailable. But then in 1971 he had strayed into another field, the controversial pastures of gyroscopic propulsion where, despite his reputation as an engineer, he had landed in hot water with his outspoken views and experiments on a subject which by its very nature challenged all that was sacred to the Establishment. As a writer in the *New Scientist* observed at the time of his ill-fated evening discourse at the Royal Institution in 1974 when he demonstrated his anti-gravity device: 'I believe he has got it wrong by changing fields too quickly and jumping to conclusions.' Despite losing considerable face over that episode he had soldiered on, building up impressive expertise and, through his own chastening experience, always willing to lend a helping hand and sympathetic ear to those attempting to assail cherished opinion. If anyone was going to give me encouragement and help then it would be Eric Laithwaite.

The one thing I didn't want to happen, however, was to get to Imperial College and then suffer the sort of mechanical failure that had aborted the demonstration for Brian Makin. I had to make certain, as far as I could, that such an embarrassment didn't happen again.

The first weeks of 1985 were, therefore, spent in giving the machine a general overhaul and tidy-up. Having run it incessantly for so long a bit of 'loose engineering' and slackness had become apparent in the system.

I replaced the bushes and bearings and fitted new ball joints. I put in new clutch linings and renewed all the belt drives. Anything that could be tightened and strengthened was dealt with accordingly. By the time I was finished I was satisfied I could do no more to make it reliable. It even looked a lot better and that, for an engineer, was important in itself. Perhaps I could now put it through its paces properly for Brian Makin before taking off for London. A few runs and I would be all set.

I shall always remember the shock I suffered when the machine refused to budge off the bench. It simply wouldn't move. Everything about it was working perfectly; the input power sources, rotational speeds, spinning of the gyros. But there was absolutely no vertical thrust. The machine had suddenly and unaccountably become a dead weight. I was shattered. Throughout February and March I tried everything I could to coax it into the air with a series of minor adjustments. But to no avail. I was getting desperate. How could I have achieved the breakthrough, proved it to my own satisfaction, and then suddenly find that the effect had mysteriously disappeared into thin air?

By this time, of course, news of my machine had become common knowledge throughout our family. Everyone had been thrilled by my success. Several were even counting on me becoming a millionaire. Now, as the bad news spread, they were coming on the phone and inquiring anxiously about the state of the machine in much the same way as they would have asked after the health of an ill relative. Janet kept issuing bulletins in hushed tones while I worked feverishly on, battling like a surgeon trying to keep a patient alive.

Twice during this period I had been in touch with Professor Laithwaite, telling him I was carrying out a few minor repairs by way of explanation for having not already kept my promise to demonstrate the machine in London. I said nothing about the disappearing force in case he thought it had never been present in the first place. Finally the professor suggested bringing the machine down on Wednesday, April 17, two days after the college returned from the Easter vacation. This gave me only ten more days to get the machine lifting again. By now all I could think of doing was running and re-running the device, hoping that by some miracle the 'goodness' would return in the same mysterious way as it had disappeared. What else could I do? The parameters of the machine had already been fixed and proved successful.

The day before we were due in London I stayed off work yet again in one last frantic attempt to restore the machine to its original power. During the morning and afternoon the garage was filled with smoke and fumes as I drove the device relentlessly on, pausing only to top up with fuel and water. Then at six o'clock, as if by magic, certainly without rhyme or reason, the machine began to rocket off the bench. I shouted to Janet and she came running from the kitchen. Together we watched it perform perfectly over several runs. I was so relieved I could have wept.

'How did you manage it?' Janet shouted above the din of the machine.

'I haven't a clue,' I said, impatiently. 'There's time to work that out later. Let's get ready for London.'

By midnight we were driving south. The machine, counterweight, vertical electric drill, and all the other bits and pieces were packed away in the boot of the car. Janet and I were accompanied by our son-in-law whose stint as night watchman had rescued me from the deadly solitude I had suffered during the latter stages of building the machine. In the process he had picked up a good bit of know-how about the device and would be of assistance in the case of an emergency at the college.

At eleven the following morning, after having lost our way in the capital, we finally drove into Imperial College in Exhibition Road in South Kensington. It gave me a tremendous thrill to step out on to the campus of one of the world's leading centres in science and technology, part of the University of London itself. I was also a little nervous. Here was I, freshly graduated from a garden shed workshop, about to show off my invention in a college which, as stated in its charter, 'provides the fullest equipment for the most advanced training and research in various branches of science . . . '

But any intimidation I may have been feeling was quickly swept away when we were greeted by the professor himself. He was a gentle giant of a man, a Lancastrian who put us immediately at ease with his natural informality. He led us into a large teaching workshop in his department where ample space had been set aside for the demonstration.

While we assembled everything the professor could hardly contain his curiosity, rolling the gyros over with his hands and lifting them up on their support arms. His face was full of boyish enthusiasm.

'I've never seen anything quite like this before,' he murmured, testing the various linkages. 'Very clever . . . very clever indeed.'

As the great man continued to make encouraging noises we put the finishing touches to the system, until finally I announced we were ready to go.

The first run was disastrous. The gyros were picking up speed nicely when, without warning, one of them broke free from its mounting, hurtled across the workshop, and bounced off the wall. My heart began to thump and my mouth went dry as I rushed up to the machine to examine the damage. Thankfully it would be a simple repair job. While the professor discreetly withdrew to his office we quickly got the wheel back into position. Half an hour later we were ready to go for a second time. I prayed that things would hold together just long enough to show the professor what the machine was capable of doing. They did. From that point everything couldn't have gone more sweetly.

On the first run we got an eight-ounce lift and by the end of the fifth were up to over twelve ounces. The professor was visibly excited. Finally he dashed out of the workshop, to reappear a minute later dragging his bewildered secretary behind him.

'Look at that,' he commanded. 'There's a machine that really works. Sandy Kidd is a remarkable man. He's actually done something that's got to be explained.'

Later, in the calm of his office, he said my machine was a potential space drive and he was prepared to act as a consultant in its future development. I could hardly believe it. The famous Professor Eric Laithwaite of Imperial College, London, a consultant to Sandy Kidd's garden shed invention! It seemed too good to be true, the sort of story you read about in boys' comics. But the professor said he meant every word of it and before we left the college promised he would arrange a meeting with someone he thought could raise the funding necessary to develop my machine. We drove back to Scotland on cloud nine.

Although I was tempted when I arrived home to investigate the mystery of how the machine had suddenly come back on song, I decided to leave well alone until after our next meeting in London with the funding agent. I was terrified in case I lost the force for a second time. Three weeks later the professor asked me to report back to the college on May 15 to demonstrate my machine to the man who might be able to raise financial backing. He was Martyn Rose, an international technology consultant who acted for various British companies overseas.

On this return visit to London we were accompanied by Ron Thompson who was anxious to assess the situation for himself. At Imperial College the professor introduced us to Mr Rose, a small, chunky man with a West Country accent who spoke fluently about the need for new energy sources and how gyroscopic propulsion was increasingly being regarded internationally as pointing the way ahead. He described himself as a 'technological midwife' who hunted around for bright ideas, then tried to marry them up to venture capital or, as he referred to it rather cynically, 'vulture' capital. Travelling extensively abroad as a consultant brought him into contact with influential people who had money to invest in promising projects such as mine. I began to tingle with excitement. This could be my big break. If only the machine could repeat its previous performance at the college.

This time things went smoothly from the very start. With Rose and Laithwaite looking on critically, the device consistently delivered a thrust of between eight and ten ounces as measured on the counterweight over half a dozen runs. Again the professor showed his enthusiasm by ducking and weaving round the machine like a schoolboy at his first physics experiment. When the demonstration ended he and Rose had an animated conversation on the merits of the device before we all repaired for lunch in the staff restaurant.

Before the meal had even been served Martyn Rose made it quite clear he was impressed with what he had just seen in the workshop and was already talking in terms of American development funding.

'America is the very place to present such an absurd idea as a reactionless motor,' he declared, as the soup arrived on the table. 'After all it is the land where dreams come true and you have a film star who is now the President and so anything is possible.'

I wasn't quite sure if absurdity was the proper basis on which to choose a country for the development of a revolutionary machine like mine. I asked about the possibility of British backing.

Rose shook his head. 'Very little chance,' he said gravely. 'It is highly unlikely that our established sources of funding would be prepared to risk money on something as fundamental as this. It's sad, but this country is perhaps the last place where this machine, if proven, would be taken up. The Americans and Japanese are the people most likely to seize on these opportunities.'

Before breaking up it was agreed that Martyn Rose would seek funding in America. When he returned to the States in three weeks' time he would take with him a complete set of explanatory papers and drawings of my device, backed by an endorsement from Professor Laithwaite. Rose seemed confident of success. 'I have a good track record in bringing clever ideas to fruition. The people I have in mind will listen to what I have to say about this machine.'

Back in Dundee I set about preparing the documentation. This had to include the cost of equipment and components for the next stage of development. It came to £7000, excluding the cost of computer space to store and process the data which would flow from a research and development programme. The budget, which covered the purchase of the variable-speed electric motors I had been unable to afford myself to drive the gyros, was extremely modest. From my point of view it was the snip of the century. But I was anxious not to scare off potential backers with fancy figures. For that reason I was also prepared to carry on my job at this stage rather than turn the project into a full-time occupation and include my North Sea oil salary as a cost within the total outlay.

In my summation I explained the many uses such a propulsion unit could be put to apart from space travel. I listed aircraft, ships and cars. I described how it would lead the way to floating camera platforms for sport, with 'magic carpets' hovering over football matches and golf tournaments. In the same fashion, it would provide for aerial inspection of buildings, marine and land survey. It would also power a range of lifting apparatus. There was no end to its application. I ended by writing: 'It would be relatively easy to improve on the results obtained from the test machine by simple alterations, but to optimize on these results, and so obtain the best power to weight ratio for the lowest input energy, it is now necessary to build a comprehensive testing facility to create a mathematical formula from which useful productive apparatus can be created.'

I duly sent my presentation package off to Imperial College where Professor Laithwaite added his endorsement of my work before forwarding everything on to Martyn Rose. His paper included the following passages:

'Mr Kidd's device has the necessary ingredient of skewed axes to be interesting in that it provides a potential "space drive" as he claims. I have seen his experimental rig and it shows sufficient promise to warrant the building of a better machine in which more adjustment of parameters is possible to enable the investigation to amplify the small effect which he has established and to enable a valuation of the full potential of such devices to be assessed.

'His machine and ideas are completely different from any device that I have ever constructed and I shall be happy to act as consultant in the design of any new machine that he proposes to build, using the "know-how" of very unconventional gyros that I have built up over the years.'

I couldn't have asked for a better recommendation from such an eminent authority. I felt like hanging it on my lounge wall. Now I could only wait and hope that Martyn Rose would bring home the bacon.

During the fortnight he was in the States I speculated endlessly on how dollar aid would be deployed. It could be used to fund a development programme in a university, either in this country or America. The funding might also be given to a private engineering and research centre. Perhaps, on the other hand, an American interest might simply buy out the concept as it stood and give me a few million bucks. Maybe. But the thought was enough to send Janet off on a mental spending spree with houses in the Bahamas and the South of France.

The question of publicity also cropped up at this stage. So far Ron Thompson had been sitting tightly on the story, maintaining strict silence. The understanding was that he would break the story at the appropriate time through a documentary programme made by Grampian Television. I asked him if that time had now arrived with Laithwaite's official support for the project.

'Not yet,' he told me firmly. 'If Rose comes up with the funding we can start filming, but not until. We must get the machine out of the shed and garage and into an official place of research to give the story the credibility we need for a programme.'

When Martyn Rose returned from America he brought encouraging news. He said he had found two potential backers, one in Chicago and the other in Sacramento. It was now a case of fixing up talks in London. I was quietly jubilant while I settled down to the waiting game once again. Two weeks later Rose told me the Americans wanted more information about the machine and the rights I was prepared to assign to them in the event of funding. They were also requesting a more realistic budget, not understanding apparently how a project of such seeming importance could be paid for by peanuts.

Unhappy at this turn of events I sent off a stiff letter to Rose. I wrote: 'To comply to all your requests as matters stand at the moment strikes me as entirely unrealistic. Surely the next stage of the negotiations must be a meeting between myself and the interested party, with you being present also, so that we can discuss needs, aims and expectations and go more fully into the financial implications of the package.

'I was indeed led to believe that such a meeting would be the next stage in the deal. Instead I am being asked to furnish yet more information about my project and commit myself to granting rights to a party whose identity and standing I still know nothing about. This I find extremely unsatisfactory. I also assumed, by the way, that the £7000 in my original estimate would be regarded as the very basic requirement for "nuts and bolts" and represented only the tip of the iceberg.'

Two days later Rose phoned to apologize for the hassle. But he said that if negotiations were to proceed he needed to know at least the rights I was prepared to grant and a revised budget, worked out on a more comprehensive basis than I had previously submitted. He said I was doing myself no favours by undercutting my requirements. I complied by sending him another letter stating that, subject to acceptable funding and a satisfactory settlement on completion of the development programme, I would be prepared to grant an option to the sponsors.

I also enclosed a new financial package, this time totalling nearly £70,000 over the first year of any agreement. To the original £7000 for basic hardware, I now added £10,000 for upgrading my workshop equipment, £25,000 in lieu of present salary, and a further £24,000 to compensate me for loss of earnings through time off and sacrifice of more lucrative employment through the years I had spent on the machine. This I considered to be an investment in kind which I was now simply reclaiming.'

Rose took off yet again for the States. When he returned at the beginning of August he said that funding now hung in the balance. The one party still interested was the venture capitalist in Sacramento but he had no intention of developing a space machine because of the enormous costs involved. He had to be assured of a commercial application for the product which would give him a quick return from a mass market.

'But there are dozens of end uses for this type of drive unit,' I protested to Rose, having previously listed all the possible applications in my original submission. 'They can even have flying motor cars if they want to relieve the congestion on their highways,' I said finally in exasperation.

Three weeks later Rose phoned again. His funding source had finally decided to proceed no further at this stage. In the final analysis he seemingly couldn't reconcile such a revolutionary device with an inventor who was non-academic and had done all the pioneering work in a shed and garage. Because of my 'amateur' status he was insisting that the results produced by the machine were scientifically verified by a university before he would take out his cheque book.

'But what about Laithwaite's commendation?' I asked sharply. 'Doesn't that count for anything?' Rose said he was sorry but could do nothing more in the meantime.

Although I was bitterly disappointed that the American exercise had failed to find me a backer, I realized Martyn Rose had done his level best. He had spent his own time and money trying to get my project off the ground. He had also discussed my work with a scientist in the States who was known to the capitalist in California. This expert had stressed the importance of finding a mathematical formula for my machine before proceeding any further and that conclusion had largely influenced the money man into backing off.

Despite the reasoning behind the final decision, I was still very frustrated that in all the dealings across the Atlantic I had never actually had an opportunity of putting my own case in my own style. Later that night, after Rose had delivered the American verdict, I picked up the phone on the spur of the moment and put a call through to the businessman in Sacramento. I just wanted to remind him that some of the greatest discoveries in the history of man had been made by people like me, with no formal qualifications, who had simply stumbled upon new ground. I new this obvious fact would change nothing. The capitalist had taken his decision on the basis of investment risk and not historical perspective. Nevertheless, I still wanted to get this point across myself. In the event he wasn't available and although I was told he would phone me back he never did.

In spite of this setback I was determined to press on under my own steam. By now I was in no state of mind to pursue the American suggestion of gaining university endorsement of my achievement. Who were they anyway, in this land where dreams were supposed to come true, to look down their noses at me because I had come out of a garden shed? Damn them all. I would build another device, one that would give even more lift than the original and therefore not be so easily ignored by potential backers. I would show them.

I might not have the grasp of mathematics and physics to work out the theory of what I had accomplished. But I had all the practical experience of the previous four years to build on. I would do it my way.

Chapter 7

It didn't take me long to decide on the design of my second machine. Although it would follow the philosophy of the first one and use all the same ingredients, this new device would be smaller, lighter, and potentially more powerful. It would also be properly engineered. This, I believed at the time, would be my final machine, so it had to be made to last and be pleasing to the eye.

These were quality standards which I simply couldn't meet with my own basic engineering resources. Even if I had been able to, I wasn't prepared to spend another two years locked away in my shed and garage. That would have pushed us all at home beyond the limits of our endurance. Besides, I was anxious to press on as quickly as possible while the trail was still hot. I decided, therefore, to have most of the components made by a local engineering company where I was well known and whose management was aware of my project. This would cost me in the region of £2800 of my own money but I considered it a worthwhile investment. Farming out work in this way would allow me to concentrate on making a rather complicated gear box for a new direct drive to the gyros, to replace the less efficient belt and pulley system of the first machine. I intended completing that task within a few weeks and then be free to assemble the other parts as they started coming in from the outside workshop. It was now September 1985. I wanted the whole thing up and running by Christmas.

I wasn't the only person, of course, who was frustrated by this latest turn of events. Ron Thompson, who had been lining up his television programme on the strength of the likely American funding, was now forced to shelve these plans for the time being. While I began once again to burn the midnight oil in my shed, his thoughts turned to other ways of gaining official status for my anti-gravity device. Laithwaite had said it was worthy of further examination and so worthy it must be. But where? And by whom? After the

American experience I preferred something nearer to home where I could have personal contact with the interested party. Dundee University was the obvious choice. We had started there with Brian Makin, but he was now abroad on an extended business trip.

Thompson and I were discussing the possibilities one evening when he suddenly remembered a couple of phrases used by Eric Laithwaite. He had said there were 'no available mathematics' to explain the phenomenon of my machine and that it represented a 'no-man's land for the physicists'.

'Physicists,' mused Thompson. 'Now I just happen to know such a person very well at our university. Name of Dr Bill Ferrier. He and I used to play cricket together in our youth. He could be the very man to help us.'

Thompson lost no time in making his move. He phoned me the following day to say that his friend would be happy to come to the garage and watch the machine go through its paces. I said I was prepared to let him see the device but not when it was running.

'That machine was built to establish a certain principle and having done so its job is now finished,' I said. 'I'm now only interested in this second machine. I'll let him see that one work when it's finished.'

Thompson protested, but I was adamant. Later I realized I had been quite irrational over this matter but at the time I was in a belligerent mood because of my disappointment over the American episode.

Dr Ferrier, however, didn't seem unduly concerned when we met the following weekend and he realized the machine had been immobilized. He spent a lot of time manipulating the device by hand, putting it through all its movements while I supplied a running commentary. He stayed three hours and took copious notes.

'It is possible you've achieved something important but I obviously can't commit myself until I've had a chance to work out some figures,' he said finally.

I had taken an instant liking to Bill with his down-to-earth, friendly manner. He was a senior lecturer at the university with a very good track record in research, having gained his doctorate for investigative work on X-ray crystallography. As a young graduate he had spent a year as a scientific officer at the Atomic Weapons Research Establishment at Aldermaston.

Two weeks after our meeting he returned empty-handed. 'I'm

sorry,' he said apologetically, 'but I simply cannot find a mathematical formula that explains what your machine is doing. There's nothing available in existing physics. My own guess if that the machine is lifting through a helicopter effect caused by the gyros being swung round like rotor blades and acting aerodynamically upon the air. We could certainly test that possibility by running the device in a vacuum chamber in one of our labs.'

'It would be a waste of time,' I said. 'I've studied helicopter theory and I can tell you right now it has nothing to do with my machine producing vertical thrust. I'm willing to bet my house against yours that this device produces a non-Newtonian force.'

Bill laughed good-naturedly. 'I'm not saying it's impossible for you to invent something new in physics. But I'll need more evidence to work on. Let's wait and see what your new model comes up with.'

By December the machine was almost ready. It weighed only two and a half pounds and stood a mere six inches off the ground. Compared to the first machine the gyros were far bigger in relation to the diameter of the crossarm. It was this factor I was counting on to give greater lift. I thought it even possible that the machine might be able to lift itself without the counterweight.

'Two and a half pounds of vertical thrust?' said Thompson incredulously. 'I can't see you getting that so quickly.'

He was right. When I started running the machine in January 1986 it didn't even register two and a half ounces. It was absolutely negative. The machine itself was running smoothly enough. The gyros, however, were rising too quickly and almost 'clapping hands' with each other at the top of their climb, but without the oomph to lift even a feather.

Again I was faced with the fickle, mysterious properties of the gyroscope. Despite my better intentions, and much against Janet's will, I plunged back once more into the old punishing routine; off to work in Aberdeen at seven in the morning, back by seven at night and into the shed until all hours. I was determined to get to the bottom of what was happening.

For the next three months I performed somersaults, changing every aspect of the machine's design and range of speeds. Nothing worked. The gyros were still shooting up without having to develop the 'muscle' to get there. There didn't seem to be enough centrifugal force acting upon the wheels. As a last resort I designed and made a twin-cylindered hydraulic pump and attached it to the main vertical shaft as a means of controlling the machine's rotational speed. Each time the gyros started to rise they would trigger off the pump whose action would then double the rotational speed from 250 to 500 rpm. This in turn would increase the centrifugal force four-fold which, hopefully, would slow down the gyros' upward movement. The mechanism worked beautifully but did nothing to check the wheels. I was now completely baffled. It was plainly obvious that although my second device was identical in principle to the first there must be something hidden in the original machine which even I wasn't aware of. That conclusion was amply confirmed when I took my first machine out of mothballs and had it producing lift again straightaway.

There was now only one thing for it. I would have to go back over the early device with a fine-tooth comb, looking for the vital clue that would solve this deepening mystery. It was only my in-built patience as a development engineer that kept my nose to the grindstone. Night after night I toiled on desperately seeking the answer. Then, suddenly, there it was staring me in the face. The missing ingredient. I had found it at last. I dashed into the house, told Janet and grabbed the phone.

'Who on earth are you calling at this hour?' she asked. 'It's almost midnight. People will be in bed.'

'Ron Thompson,' I said. 'I must tell him right away. He's been pretty anxious about this whole thing as well.'

Ten minutes later Thompson barged through the front door, dishevelled but curious. Within seconds I was telling him how my first machine was producing its vertical thrust for a different set of reasons than I had ever intended. In other words, I had created something by mistake. The main component of the machine's success was never meant to have been there in the first place.

'The key to the mystery lies in flexibility,' I told Thompson, who now had a reasonable working knowledge of the project. 'Without me ever being properly aware of it, the main vertical shaft becomes slack in its top and bottom mountings due to the constant rotational movement of the device. This means that when it spins round, the shaft wobbles about, constantly varying the radius of the gyros on the crossarm. In other words the distance of the gyros from the central shaft keeps altering.'

'What difference does that make?' asked Thompson with a frown.

'Well, it's now my theory that when the gyro finds that its

49

radius has suddenly shortened it can overcome the centrifugal force and rise upwards. But when the radius lengthens again as the shaft flexes away from it, the gyro is slammed back out by the resultant increase in centrifugal force. At that precise moment the gyro releases a force to give the machine its lifting action. The gyros are going through this pattern of movement alternately at such lightning speed that the thrust comes out as a continuous force.'

'So the gyros release their force on the way out and not as you previously believed on the way in,' Thompson observed.

'That's right. This discovery also explains why the machine gave us all that trouble just prior to its first demonstration in London. While overhauling it I had tightened up the main shaft and destroyed the one factor that made the whole thing work. It was only when the shaft worked itself loose again that the thrust reappeared.'

Thompson looked thoughtful. 'It's also easier to understand now why Martyn Rose was unable to pull it off with the Americans,' he remarked. 'The papers you submitted didn't really contain the proper explanation of how the machine produced lift. He deserves an apology. The Americans must have been racking their brains trying to fathom the whole thing out. The same with Bill Ferrier. Neither of them had Laithwaite's advantage of actually seeing the machine perform.'

I couldn't sleep that night for thinking how luck had played such an important part in what I had achieved. If the machine had been properly engineered in the first place, with the main shaft firmly in position, it would never have produced the lifting effect and I would have been forced to abandon my anti-gravity dream. I always said that my original device was a load of old junk! What I had to do now seemed perfectly clear. Build yet another machine, one in which the flexibility factor would be engineered into its design. I would simulate the wobbling effect by fitting eccentrics to the main shaft and attaching them to the top arms holding up the gyros. An eccentric is an off-centre rotating disc, an odd piece of mechanism which causes anything attached to it to be pulled in and then released. If both my gyros were subjected to this action simultaneously they should produce their thrust in the form of a pulsing action.

I started building Machine Number Three in the spring of 1986. I was now in a much happier frame of mind, convinced that I was on the right track at last. I also felt certain that it wouldn't be long before another interested party appeared on the horizon. My premonition was well founded. A month later Ron Thompson told me that a professor in the mechanical engineering department at Edinburgh University would like to meet me and watch my original machine in action. He was Professor Joe McGeough, Regius Professor of Engineering, who had heard of my work from Thompson when they had shared a table at a private function in Edinburgh several months previously.

Although I had vowed not to demonstrate my first prototype again, I relented on the spur of the moment and agreed to the meeting. He would be the third professor to examine my machine in eighteen months. But, as with Brian Makin, when he came to the garage, the gremlins again prevented my latest academic from seeing it produce lift, this time because of a faulty carburettor in the gyro engine.

The conversation in the house later followed the same lines as the one with Makin. Whenever I mentioned breaking Newton's Third Law the distinguished professor from Edinburgh became decidedly edgy.

'You musn't speak like that,' he scolded me. 'If you do people will not take you seriously.'

Once again I had been made to feel that if I pursued this rebellious line I would never get to heaven. The professor, however, seemed intrigued by the machine and went on to speak about the importance of identifying its possible commercial applications for the purpose of enlisting the support of a funding agency.

He said his university had a department called Unived Technology to exploit new ideas and a laboratory which specialized in dynamics, a branch of engineering which applied to a machine like mine. No promises were made on the spot but when Thompson contacted the professor several days later Joe McGeough said he had already spoken to the university authorities and despite my lack of formal qualifications a place could be found for me in his department on a research project. He said he was prepared to write a paper about the machine and submit it to the British Technology Group, with whom he had previously dealt, as an application for funding.

This was an independent, self-funding organization and combined the activities of the National Enterprise Board and the National Research Development Corporation. Its main role was to promote the development and exploitation of new technology throughout British industry. One of its publications was a glossy booklet entitled

Help for the Inventor. On page one under the heading 'Is it Feasible?' was the following warning: 'Are you sure that your invention doesn't contradict any of the natural laws that seem to apply to the world as we know it, laws like energy conservation (you can't get energy from nowhere, only convert it from one form to another) or Newton's laws (in particular the third, which says that action and reaction are equal and opposite)? Perhaps you had no intention of inventing a perpetual motion machine or an anti-gravity device, but there are still quite a few people with ambitions in those directions. These are extremes, but maybe your idea just isn't practical, although there are no theoretical reasons why it shouldn't work.'

' "No theoretical reasons why it shouldn't work!" ' I howled at Janet. 'I've got news for them. I have a machine that hasn't heard of theory and does work.' I threw the brochure down. It struck me as another blatant example of minds already closed to the possibility of fundamental change. How could they encourage new ideas and at the same time say that ancient laws musn't be challenged? It was ludicrous. However, the speed of the professor's response had put me in an embarrassing position. I was conscious of the fact that Bill Ferrier was still waiting in the wings. Out of fairness I must now offer him the demonstration of the original machine which he had earlier been denied. It was only right that he was given first option to take it further if he wished.

Two days later, by which time I had repaired the faulty carburettor, Bill Ferrier came to the garage. This time there were no hitches. The machine was at its best, registering a lift of over twelve ounces. Throughout the session his eyes remained glued to the bench where the device hovered effortlessly over its surface against the counterweight. He seemed mesmerized by what was happening. This was how I had described it all to him the previous year. Now he had the evidence of his own eyes, along with the additional information I gave him about the varying radius on the crossarm caused by the movement of the central shaft.

'I'm shattered by what I've just seen,' he told me later in the house. 'According to the physics I've always known, your machine shouldn't be able to do that. Yet there it is. There has got to be an answer and I'll not be able to rest until I find it.'

He now readily dismissed his earlier theory of helicopter lift. But to eliminate all possibility of such an effect I agreed to his suggestion that we test the machine with the gyros fitted with wooden covers to isolate them from contact with the atmosphere. If the device still lifted, Bill said, it would be all the proof we needed that the gyros were not reacting on air. The vacuum chamber experiment he had previously proposed was no longer necessary. A few days later, with the shrouds in position, the machine glided off the bench without a second thought.

Bill Ferrier was now pressing on in a fresh attempt to work out a mathematical formula on the basis of all the new evidence. He warned that this could take a considerable time. But in the meantime he agreed to give me a written endorsement of my machine. On university-headed notepaper, dated July 7, 1986, he wrote:

> I first met Mr A.D. Kidd when, just over a year ago, I was asked to look at a paper by him on a device to produce vertical lift using centrifugally-mounted high speed gyros. After I had read the paper and seen the machine I was convinced it would not work. Mr Kidd, however, was then working on an improved machine and was undeterred by my criticism. Some three months ago Mr Kidd returned to his original machine and, for the first time, I saw it in operation. There is no doubt that the machine does produce vertical lift. Several modifications were then made at my suggestions in order to disprove other possibilities of lift, particularly aerodynamic effects.
>
> I am fully satisfied that this device needs further research and development. I have expressed myself willing to help Mr Kidd whose engineering ability is beyond question, and for whom I now have the greatest respect. I am currently trying to interest the university in housing the development and also in finding 'enterprise' money to fund the next stage.
>
> I do not as yet understand why this device works. But it does work! The importance of this is probably obvious to the reader but, if it is not, let me just say that the technological possibilities of such a device are enormous. Its commercial exploitation must be worth millions.

This was more, much more, than I had ever expected. I was really taken aback by such unstinted praise. Together with Professor Laithwaite's testimony, I now had the makings of a dossier with which to start chipping away at the barriers of prejudice. Bill

Ferrier's use of the word 'millions' would also be certain to interest my family.

When Ron Thompson saw this latest endorsement he decided the time had come to invite Dundee University to take my machine under its wing. After all, he argued, we now had glowing reports from two academics in different disciplines, based at different universities, who had more or less come to the same conclusion independently. I agreed with his reasoning. I could also detect his growing anxiety over the television programme. He confessed, in fact, he was having nightmares over the story breaking before he could get the documentary made and transmitted.

Within days of his approach through private contacts, the university agreed to undertake a research project lasting up to a year. I heard the news when I got home from work late in the evening. Ron was already waiting for me in the house. Janet was jumping about like a grasshopper.

'We're going shopping tomorrow,' was how she greeted me as I came in through the front door.

'Shopping?' I said, puzzled by her obvious excitement.

'Yes, shopping,' she repeated laughingly. 'We're going to buy you a mortar board and gown.' Then it dawned on me. We had broken the ice at last. I was about to come in from the cold.

★ ★ ★ ★ ★

These were hard times for the universities, which had been hit by cutbacks in central government funding. They were having to count their pennies as never before. Projects had to be carefully scrutinized before being funded. On the other hand, universities were now being encouraged to earn more money for themselves through research projects leading to lucrative spin-off contracts with manufacturing companies. Backing a project like mine would also bring immense academic prestige to any institution which could successfully pioneer the development of such a fundamental concept as anti-gravity propulsion.

The Dundee University official responsible at that time for negotiating external contracts was Graham Thomson, Director of Industrial Liaison. He had previously been managing director of the Timex manufacturing plant in the City and a vice-president of the American-based corporation. He was a local man 'made good'.

We had our first meeting in July 1986. I could tell he was enthusiastic about the project and he promised to make my entry into the university as smooth as possible.

He explained that the university would probably finance the first twelve months of the programme before bringing in an outside funding body for later development work. This would allow the project to get off to a quick start. Bill Ferrier had already indicated the manpower requirements. He, as the physicist, would be the team leader. There would also be a mechanical engineer, a laboratory technician, and myself. Later we might require a part-time secretary to collate the stream of data that would result from the various test procedures.

Graham Thomson also explained that it was vital to file an application for a patent on the machine at the Patent Office in London before work could begin. Although the full process of obtaining a patent could take up to four and a half years in the United Kingdom, the invention was initially protected from the date the application was filed, with full rights being obtained upon the patent being granted.

Before a patent was granted, however, the application was scrutinized to make certain it fulfilled three basic requirements. The invention must be new, involve an inventive step, and be capable of industrial application. A patent office examiner would conduct a thorough search and examination of all pertinent records to make sure that these conditions could be met.

Although the official literature makes no mention of it, applications are screened on grounds of national interest. Under a little-known section of the Patents Act, 1977, the Ministry of Defence has sweeping powers to 'call in' inventions in the interests of national security. They have a special department sifting through all new ideas which could possibly fall into this category. While an application is being vetted in this way, the inventor is warned that he/she must not talk about the invention or enter into any form of publicity. Failure to comply can result in a two-year jail sentence. Only when the application is declassified, as most eventually are, can the inventor speak freely about his/her brainchild.

Applications which are subjected to such detailed examination form only a small fraction of the 37,000 which arrive at the Patent Office every year. But when they do land on the desk, the security branch of the organization swings into action. Such a case had been highlighted in a national newspaper. A Cheshire man who claimed he had invented a non-nuclear method of generating electricity had received the dreaded phone call within hours of his application arriving in London. He was told to keep his lips sealed. A few days later a letter arrived telling him his application had been passed to the ministry. In the event his idea was not considered a threat to the national interest.

But this sensitive aspect of my machine had always concerned me. Its military implications could be devastating, particularly in the field of nuclear warfare where no defence system anywhere could counteract the speed of a warhead being delivered by a space vehicle under constant acceleration. My fears on this point were largely shared by Bill Ferrier. It was conceivable that the government could step in and confiscate my machine. However, that hurdle was a long way off and other events were to dominate the future, and the fortunes, of my anti-gravity invention.

Several days after Graham Thomson had been to see me, Bill Ferrier appeared on my doorstep in an obviously excited state of mind.

'I think I've got it,' he announced briskly, following me into the lounge. 'I think I have the basis of a formula that will fit the theory. But to start finding the answers I've had to turn physics on its head. I've had to be as unorthodox in my approach to the equations as you have been with your machine.' He paused to gain breath. 'I was sitting at home a short time ago trying for the umpteenth time to find a starting point when the answer struck me like a thunderbolt.'

'Does it lie within the present scope of physics?' I asked.

'Yes, it does,' said Bill firmly. 'The answers are there all right. It's just a case of working them out to meet a situation that has never arisen before. But, as I suspected, it's going to be a long, complicated business.'

Before leaving me that Sunday night Bill explained he was going south on business but when he returned the following weekend he would help me prepare all the information required for the patent application.

The next day I was browsing through the local library when my eye caught the title of a book called *A Step Farther Out*, written by Jerry Pournelle, an American who had been a space scientist and was now a writer specializing in space technology and space fiction. Flicking through the pages I noticed he made several references to my type of machine and that someday he believed man would possibly develop space drives to give us speeds faster than light. But he emphasized that would-be inventors must build devices that work and not simply draw up plans and theories. He seemed to be on my side.

Ron Thompson decided to phone him at his home in California and tell him about my machine. Pournelle listened politely but said that from long and bitter experience in such matters he would only believe that an anti-gravity device really worked if he saw it with his own eyes. He had been all over America in his day looking at 'miracle' devices which had all turned out to be bum steers. He said that such an effect could be created by simply jumping up and down on a set of scales at certain frequencies which would fool the mechanism into thinking you were lighter than you really were.

The American author said that only by subjecting the machine to any one of three tests could it really be established whether the device was genuine or not. The first of these involved hanging the machine from the roof on a length of string before setting it in motion. If the thrust created was sufficient to displace it from the vertical and keep it there for up to a minute at an angle to the ground then that would prove the force was real. The second test was similar to the one used by Eric Laithwaite at his Royal Institution demonstration. Run the device on a spring scale to see if it loses weight. The third method was rather crude. 'Take the machine to a high building with another object of exactly the same weight,' he had said, 'then throw the two of them over the side simultaneously after starting up the machine. If the gizmo hits the ground last then you've made it.'

I was not amused when I heard of Pournelle's suspicious reaction to my machine. He hadn't really been interested to hear what Laithwaite or Ferrier had said about it. The fact was that he hadn't seen it for himself and so there was no way he was going to believe anything. I took his point to a certain extent, but he could have spared me the details of the 'suicide' test.

'God almighty,' I shouted. 'Is he really suggesting I drop it from a great height and smash it to smithereens? The man must think I'm a fool. That's not the kind of smash hit I'm after.'

I was still seething over what he had said when Bill Ferrier's wife, Nancy, came rushing on the phone the next day. Bill had been taken ill while in the south but had insisted on driving home from Manchester to reach his own bed. His condition, however, had so deteriorated by the time he reached Dundee that he had been admitted to hospital with a suspected heart condition. Eight days later he was released but told he would have to return for a series of tests. On the first night he was home he asked me over to discuss the patent application and other aspects of our programme. I was amazed that, in the circumstances, his first thoughts were still on the machine.

I found him in a chirpy mood. He told me he was ninety per cent certain of the project's success. I expressed the hope that his illness would not prevent him being involved in the research. He paused before replying. 'I fully intend being with you on that plane to Sweden when you go to pick up your Nobel Prize for Physics.' I looked at him sharply. He was not smiling. He was serious.

I never saw Bill again after that night. He died a week later at the age of fifty-five after collapsing in his garden. His obituary in the local newspaper spoke of his valuable work for the university and beyond, describing him as a popular figure who would be very badly missed. Needless to say I was shattered. Not only had he become my friend. We had formed a good working relationship based on mutual respect for each other's ability. He actually believed in what I was trying to achieve. In a sense we had been explorers together setting out on the same expedition. Now the leader had gone. I was, quite frankly, devastated.

Chapter 8

After the first few days following Bill Ferrier's death, when the numbness had started to wear off, I began to speculate about the future of my university project. Would it carry on under another person or would it be scrapped altogether? After all, it was Bill's optimism over the machine's potential that had largely persuaded the university to back it in the first place. Now, without his driving force, the original commitment might be allowed to die too. But the university didn't hesitate.

Within a fortnight they told me that the research and development programme would go ahead under the supervision of another, as yet unnamed, member of the physics department. Obviously I was greatly relieved at this news. What now concerned me, however, was not the inevitable delay there was bound to be in getting started, but the difficulty in finding a replacement for Bill who would have the same enthusiasm and belief in my cause.

I had the feeling I would finish up having to do my missionary act with whomever was asked to step into the breach. So it was to be. From the moment we met, James Thomson, who had been a colleague of Bill Ferrier's, made little attempt to disguise his suspicion of my machine. He simply would not accept my explanation of how the gyros were producing their vertical thrust. He attempted to disprove my theory by working out equations to show that such a pattern of forces was physically impossible.

Despite seeing the device lift for himself, and agreeing it was creating some kind of force, he was almost certain there would be an ordinary mechanical explanation for the effect being produced, such as vibration, friction, or aerodynamics. Eventually I told him after much argument that even if he used all the vibration, friction, resonance, and every other weird effect known to engineering and physics, he could never build a machine to do the same as mine.

It quickly became obvious our attitudes could never be reconciled. He was sticking to his guns and I was sticking to mine. At one stage he turned up at the garage with a set of graded weights which he attached to the counterbalance to get a more scientific measurement of the machine's thrust. He obviously felt that my method of using small spanners attached to a magnet, which had served their purpose adequately in the hallowed surroundings of Imperial College, was simply not good enough. This was just one example of how we clashed; the classical scholar versus the rebellious, non-academic innovator.

The final straw came after six weeks at a meeting in Graham Thomson's office to investigate the possibility of filing a patent application for my invention. Present was Dr Robert Naismith, a patent agent representing a Glasgow firm who were acting for the university. No sooner had the session started when Jimmy Thomson stunned everyone by announcing he could not at that stage associate himself with any document which supported the claim being made for my device. He again repeated the view that in all probability the machine was nothing new. It was premature, he said, for the university to invest funds in a research project before other possible reasons for the machine's behaviour had been duly eliminated.

This seemed to me to be an attempt to pre-empt the official project in the university with an unofficial one in my garage. This process could go on for years. I had already been through the garage routine and was now anxious to advance into a more sophisticated environment. That was the whole idea of the present exercise. Naturally I was upset that Jimmy Thomson had chosen this moment to throw a spanner in the works and I was determined to dig in my heels if need be. Dr Naismith shuffled his papers in embarrassment. He had expected to receive details of the machine and how it was believed to work and not to find himself in the middle of a dispute over the merits of the invention.

Finally Graham Thomson broke the awkward silence. 'We'll go ahead and draw up the application on the basis of the information supplied by Bill Ferrier and Sandy,' he declared firmly. 'It also fits in with the findings of Eric Laithwaite.'

By the time the meeting ended it was quite clear to everyone that Jimmy Thomson and I were incompatible and shortly afterwards the Industrial Liaison Department agreed to my request that he be replaced by another member of the academic staff.

Graham Thomson had by now drawn up a timetable for the twelve-month project. It was divided into three segments. The first, under the heading of 'feasibility', would establish what the long-term commitment was likely to be in terms of manpower and funding. This would take three months and involve basic testing of the machine. The next stage, called 'Prototype', would also last three months. During this period test rigs would be built to evaluate the full potential of the invention, provided the initial tests confirmed the presence of a force and the university believed they could provide the resources to exploit the possibilities. The last phase would deal with 'Finalized Design'. If the machine's output could be mathematically powered up to a realistic level, the final six months would be devoted to designing a prototype capable of reproducing these findings.

It was stipulated that progress from one stage to another would depend on a successful conclusion to the previous phase. This was the same rule as applied to students with their degree exams, but without the benefit of resits. In adopting this cautious approach to a highly contentious project the university was also being financially prudent by not giving a blank-cheque commitment to the whole twelve months. The budget for each segment would, therefore, be fixed separately. I was asked to submit a costing for the initial three-month period.

On the basis that support staff and workshop facilities were being provided 'in house', I contained expenditure to £400 for certain components, plus my fee of just over £6000, this being one quarter of the salary I was then earning as an electrical design supervisor. I realized that by setting my remuneration at this level I was asking for the sort of money they were paying professors. But if I was expected to give up my job to allow the university to develop my invention, then they would have to sustain me at my current level of earnings.

I felt even more justified in adopting this bullish attitude in the light of the results I had just obtained from Machine Number Three. The eccentrics, replicating the flexibility of the wobbly shaft, had produced the desired effect. The device was producing lift, not as much as the original prototype, but doing it with a very definite pulsing movement, which was a sure sign the gyros were releasing their energy together each time they were pulled back out from the central shaft. This, of course, had been my prediction. I was jubilant.

I was now also convinced that at a certain stage of their inward movement, just at the point they were balancing out the centrifugal force, the gyros were momentarily losing their inertial mass, the energy weight they had gained under rotation. According to all the theories I knew this was meant to be impossible and anything I said to the contrary would be regarded as even more treasonable than claiming to break Newton's Third Law. But I was now more certain than ever that other people's understanding of the way gryoscopes behaved, as based on the textbooks, was totally wrong.

The machine itself was a real beauty to look at. It was smaller than the first but bigger than the second and, at just over two pounds, lighter than both. I played with it for hours, firing it up until it became a blurred mass of spinning metal, light spots dancing off the shiny surfaces like sparks flowing from a meteorite plunging through space. There was almost an ethereal look about this latest machine. The only change I now wanted to make was to transfer the eccentrics from the top arms to the bottom of the lower support arms to allow the gyros greater freedom of movement as they moved inwards. This, I believed, would increase the lift factor.

In view of all the new evidence from my latest machine I felt it imperative that the patent application be revised to include this information. Fortunately the original version had not yet been sent off to London, so this could readily be done, although a start to the research project would now be delayed still further. Dr Naismith came to my home for a late-night session towards the end of November to review and discuss the additional evidence. He said he did not have to see any of my machines in action. It was no part of his function to verify or disprove what the inventor claimed he had done and then form judgements. He was simply there to take down evidence like a solicitor and present that information in the most professional way he could to safeguard the interests of his client. Nevertheless, he explained that he should satisfy himself that the structure was technically feasible. In doing so he considered that the endorsements from Eric Laithwaite and Bill Ferrier provided credibility to the claim for industrial applicability, although this aspect of the application would also be scrutinized by the patent examiner.

In his report to the Industrial Liaison Department on the final wording of the application Dr Naismith wrote:

'During our discussion Mr Kidd raised a number of technical issues which appeared quite controversial. For example, during the operation of the modified apparatus there is no mass in the gyroscopic precession. As you will no doubt appreciate, these comments are very radical and after discussing the matter with

Mr Kidd I decided that it would be inappropriate at the present time to include such a disclosure in the specification without having verification. Although it is desirable to explain the exact operation of a structure disclosed in a patent, this does not necessarily extend to including theories which are unverified. It is sufficient to describe the structure and to explain in general terms how the operation of the structure produces an end result, that is, the provision of thrust at the upper bearing and I believe that is all that is required at this stage. Mr Kidd advised me that he had constructed a prototype that works and accordingly the invention would appear to be capable of industrial application.'

The patent specification ran to ten pages of descriptive narrative and included three diagrams. The language was obviously very technical, although there was the occasional phrase which conveyed the excitement of what the machine was really all about: ' . . . the present invention relates to gyroscopic devices having application as a prime mover on land, water or in space . . . It is believed to be particularly advantageous in space where the force of gravity and friction is minimal . . . '

The more I read these words the more they seemed to jump out at me from the pages of the typescript. 'They're ready made for the censor,' I remarked glumly to Janet. 'I simply can't see how we can escape classification.'

She nodded her agreement. 'Yes, the men in the shabby raincoats will be arriving at the door any day now.'

Even the patent agent said there was a good chance of the Ministry of Defence calling in the application because of the machine's military implications. The future progress of my work depended entirely on the machine being registered in the normal way. It was a frightening thought.

The documentation was finally despatched to the Patent Office in early December. With Christmas mail now starting to arrive at the house there was a frantic sifting through of envelopes each day to find the official-looking one which would bring us the vital news. Finally it arrived from the university, enclosing a copy of the letter received from the patent agent. It simply read: 'New British Patent Application No. 8629405. Alexander Duncan Kidd. Gyroscopic Thrust Apparatus. We are pleased to confirm the filing of the new patent application numbered as above at the Patent Office on

December 9, 1986. The official filing receipt is enclosed for your safekeeping.' I was through the net. There had been no security clampdown after all. My sigh of relief must have been heard all the way to London.

Two days before Christmas Graham Thomson sent me a letter of engagement. My terms were being met for the first stage of the research programme which would run from February 1, 1987, to April 30, 1987. The funding was being classified as a 'Research Fellowship'. The person assigned to work with me was Dr Ian Davidson, a lecturer in mechanical engineering who was a specialist in dynamics. It became apparent shortly afterwards, however, that the overlord of the project was going to be Professor Brian Makin, head of the Department of Electrical Engineering and Electronics, who had been the first academic to learn about my work two years before when he had been brought to my garage by Ron Thompson. A burned out clutch on the gyro engine had prevented him seeing the machine produce its thrust. Since then, of course, he had read the reports of Professor Laithwaite and Dr Ferrier based on their observations of the device actually generating lift. Being of independent mind, however, Professor Makin would require his own first-hand evidence before formulating an opinion.

But all this was in the future. For the present it was the festive season of 1986 and the Kidd household had much to celebrate. Dad would shortly be off to university as a Research Fellow. I tell you, I had to take a lot of ribbing from family and friends over that job description. I knew what my father would have said if he had known: 'I don't care what they call you son. Remember you're a real engineer. *Just make things, and make them work.*'

Chapter 9

I was, of course, well aware that university life would be an entirely new experience for me. How could it be otherwise? I had been brought up in the hurly-burly of private industry with its deadlines, disciplines, and all-important profit margins. A world of clocking in and clocking out, workers and bosses, them and us, and the ever-present threat of sanctions if you stepped out of line.

Now I suddenly found myself in a timeless sort of society with its own distinctive set of values built up through centuries of tradition. This was the up-market end of the learning industry where staff and students were left largely on trust to get on with their tasks. You still, of course, had a pecking order but it wasn't so blatantly paraded as in factories and engineering workshops. It wasn't recognizable by the way people dressed or spoke or by the state of their hands. Professors, as I was to find out for myself, were not like foremen, prowling around keeping a constant eye on things and chivvying people on. Certainly, a wind of change was starting to blow through the campus when I arrived on the scene, due to the government's crackdown on cash. But deeply-ingrained attitudes of mind were not going to change overnight simply because the University Grants Commission was after better value for money.

I spent the first few days wandering round the engineering department getting accustomed to new places and faces and trying very hard to ease myself into this strange, alien atmosphere called academic freedom. I had been allocated room number J7 in a long corridor populated by lecturers. The first thing I did was to measure it. The room was bigger than my shed and a damned sight more comfortable. The second thing I did was to lean back in my swivel chair, pick up the phone and put a call through to Janet. 'This is the Research Fellow calling,' I announced in mock seriousness. Then I took a leisurely stroll across the quadrangle to reflect once more on the series of events which had brought about my graduation from a garden shed to a university campus.

Having already met Dr Ian Davidson and discussed the project, I now submitted a lengthy report to Professor Makin detailing all the observational evidence I had gleaned so far from my three machines and enclosing all the relevant drawings. I suggested that I should be allowed to build a fourth machine in which the eccentrics would be moved from the top arms to the gyros' lower supports to allow the wheels greater freedom as they moved inwards during precession. It had already been stipulated that the first phase of the project would include the testing of my machine. But which machine? I was determined it wouldn't be the original version because of the flukey, accidental way it produced its vertical thrust. It made far more sense to build a new model for the test, a machine into which every known characteristic of behaviour could be properly engineered.

Replying by memo, Brian Makin agreed with my proposal. 'My personal views are that your ideas should be tried and we must agree to a list of objectives with a corresponding programme.' He suggested that the new machine should be powered by two variable-speed electric motors, one for driving the device, the other for the gyros. He said that changes in the level of the forces generated within the machine's structure would be measured by fitting strain gauges to the gyro support arms. This I knew to be the normal way of carrying out such an analysis. Strain gauges are small devices which register the slightest change in stress and strain by sending an electrical signal to a computer where it can be measured and displayed on a counter. The professor also pointed out that a decision on the commercial viability of my machine would have to be taken by the deadline of April 30 set for the first phase. I would, he said, have free access to the engineering workshops. End of message.

I sat for some time at my desk studying the memo. Something was missing. Something very fundamental to the whole exercise. There was no mention of the support team proposed by Bill Ferrier. No physicist, no mechanical engineer and no laboratory technician properly assigned to the project. I was being given access to a workshop and I could have discussions with a lecturer already involved with his own responsibilities. But nothing more it seemed. I refused to believe that this constituted a proper research and development programme and in the following days I kept thinking that others would be seconded to the task. But the university authorities made no move. Then finally it dawned on me there was to be no backup after all. I was on my own. I didn't know whether to laugh or cry.

After several weeks I got the feeling I was being slowly abandoned until it became painfully obvious that my machine and I were simply an embarrassment to the university.

No one really wanted to know about the project. The man who had supported my cause so enthusiastically was now no more and with his death everything had somehow become second-hand. The university, it appeared to me, was simply going through the motions of honouring their commitment but with no serious intention of really exploring the potential of my revolutionary device. As my contact with the academics grew less frequent, I found myself spending more and more time in the workshops making the various parts for my new machine and mixing with technicians who spoke my kind of language. I was stranded within an establishment which had all the expertise necessary to determine the value of my machine. It was like starving to death in a warehouse full of food.

In the meantime I decided to honour my promise to Professor Joe McGeough at Edinburgh University to give him a demonstration of my first machine. His previous attempt to see it work in my garage had been marred by engine failure. I had, of course, at that time turned down his offer to approach the British Technology Group for a funding project at his university because of my preference for Dundee, a decision which he had taken in good part. Now, he said he would make arrangements to have the machine displayed in his department.

A technician was standing by to help me when I arrived at The King's Buildings on the south side of the city. We quickly got the machine assembled with its counterweight in an unoccupied laboratory and rigged up the fuel and water lines. Within half an hour I was ready to go. The professor arrived with two of his colleagues, one a physicist, the other a mechanical engineer who specialized in dynamics. Everything went like a dream with the machine producing its thrust effortlessly each time I got the gyros up to their optimum speed. No one spoke. I simply kept putting the machine through one run after another. Each time it lifted my spirits soared as well.

Suddenly I became aware that another person had entered the laboratory to join the small group gathered round the machine. He was a tall, angular man, casually dressed with hawk-like features. Although obviously known to the others, it was apparent he had not been officially invited to the demonstration. How he ever knew what was happening in that particular laboratory at that precise time I never found out. But he proceeded to watch the machine over several runs before introducing himself as Professor Stephen Salter, the university's professor of engineering design.

I knew who he was right away. Salter had made a name for himself in the 1970s by attempting to prove that commercial electricity could be safely and cheaply generated by exploiting the power of sea waves. His experimental wave-energy project had been highly regarded in many quarters before the government had pulled the plug on funding, allegedly because of pressure being applied by the nuclear lobby. The professor had designed a special machine for his project which bobbed about the water like a nodding duck, later to become widely known as 'Salter Ducks'. These devices involved the use of gyroscopes based on conventional physics theory as invented by Otto Schlick. So, for no other reason than that alone, he was now intrigued by what he saw.

When I finished my final run and stepped back from the bench, the academics began to question me about the way I thought the machine produced its force. I gave them the benefit of my opinion, ending mischievously by suggesting they would understand these things better than a shop floor engineer like myself.

'Don't come that line,' Salter interrupted in a reprimanding tone. 'We know you are a very clever fellow.' I smiled at the compliment.

The first to pass judgement was the dynamics man. 'It is my opinion,' he said solemnly, 'that the whole force is simply being generated by vibration. It is a secondary effect and nothing more.'

By now I was starting to take such a reaction in my stride. 'Is that so?' I replied in a calm, measured voice. 'Are you saying this because you can think of no other explanation which you would find acceptable?' There was a pause.

'Yes,' he said finally. 'It would be true to say that.'

The frankness of his reply took me aback, but not so much as the statement which followed from Professor Salter.

'You can believe that if you wish,' he said firmly, 'but if you eliminate all the secondary possibilities such as vibration then what you have here is worthy of the Nobel Prize for Physics.'

You could have heard a pin drop as he then turned on his heels and walked smartly out of the laboratory. A few minutes later he returned to give me three small electric motors which he thought might be helpful in my work.

Throughout this postmortem Professor McGeough had remained

silent. His face had gone white with tension. He seemed ill at ease and did not pronounce on my machine in any way. He simply advised me in a low, grim voice to get the device covered up and back to Dundee and to keep it there until the project had been completed. I have never seen Joe McGeough since that morning of high drama.

Driving back along the motorway I couldn't help reflecting on the irony of how no one at Dundee University had yet asked to be given a similar demonstration of my first machine. That, I thought, would have been the natural thing to do at the outset of the project. But it was fully two months into the first phase before I was eventually asked to bring it in for appraisal. When I did so, Dr Davidson was the only academic who turned up and saw it produce its lifting force. It was then decided to put the original device through the strain gauge tests and not the latest one. This was precisely what I had wanted to avoid but, with only four weeks now left of the feasibility stage and still no results obtained, there was simply no time to argue.

I was told to hunt around for a variable-speed electric motor fast enough to drive the gyros. My $6\frac{1}{2}$ cc internal combustion engine wasn't acceptable on grounds of noise, exhaust fumes and possible vibration. I was unable, however, to find a suitable motor within the time at my disposal. The only thing left was to use the slower electric motor already in the department and adapt my machine accordingly. This meant, among other adjustments, fitting bigger gyros which would require less speed. But in doing this I upset the geometry of the device and destroyed its force. It became a lead balloon. I was furious. A machine which had entered the university in sound working order was now no longer functioning through no fault of mine. It was like going into a hospital for routine tests and coming out half dead.

When I complained bitterly to Ian Davidson it was decided to restore the machine to its original specification and revert to the liquid fuel engine despite all its deficiencies. In the event I was able largely to overcome the hazards of fumes and noise by using a vacuum cleaner to suck the engine's effluent through an empty oil drum, thereby allowing the oil content of the vapour to drain off. To meet all this extra work the university agreed to extend phase one by a month, now giving me a deadline at the end of May. With only a week to go the machine was ready for testing with strain gauges in position. Several days later the test was performed without a hitch and the device duly registered a small positive force. That evening

I took a copy of the pen recording home to show Janet. Spreading the long strip of paper across the coffee table in the lounge, I pointed out how the line on the graph swung sharply upwards when the gryos reached a certain speed and then levelled out to maintain an elevated hight to denote the thrust. 'That,' I said, rolling up the graph carefully, 'is possibly the only recording of its kind for a machine like this anywhere in the world.' The fact was, however, that the test had told me nothing I didn't know already. It had given no clue as to how the machine was producing its thrust. I had my own ideas, of course, which could have been confirmed by using high-speed photography or laser scans to construct a visual picture of the gyros' behaviour. Bill Ferrier had spoken about doing this. No one else had mentioned the possibility.

Later that week, on the morning of June 2, 1987, I drove from home to the university as usual, parked the car, then sauntered across the campus towards my office in the engineering block. It was a warm, sunny day and there was no need to hurry. I could do nothing more until the university decided on the next step. They had wasted no time, however, in making up their minds. Ten minutes after I had reached my desk the phone rang. It was the secretary in the Industrial Liaison Department asking if I would come right away to see the director.

This was it. I didn't quite know what to expect as I set out once more to cross the precinct, this time heading for the main tower block which housed the administration. Graham Thomson looked up from his desk as I entered the room and gestured towards an empty chair. He looked unhappy and I didn't have to be a clairvoyant to sense the news was not good.

'I'm sorry, Sandy,' he said gravely, without beating about the bush, 'but the university is pulling out of the project. The reason is lack of money. We don't feel justified in devoting further scarce resources to investigating your machine.'

In that moment I felt only a sense of numbness and was lost for words. I could only gaze blankly at the wall, thinking how I had never been in this position before. Dismissed on the spot for reasons beyond my control. The decision had been taken following a report submitted by Ian Davidson. This stated that although preliminary tests had been conducted and a force recorded, the maximum effect was very small. The report went on: 'On the basis of the slow progress so far it would be unrealistic to expect any definitive statement about the way in which the effect is generated in a time

70

scale of less than three months. All that can be said at the moment is that there is an effect and it is small. Because the mechanism is not understood, predicting it or how the effect might be enhanced is not possible at this stage. I am still not convinced that there is anything other than some complex interaction between the device and its supporting structure.'

By now I was angry. Although I had long realized the university's heart was not in the project, I was still stunned by this sudden turn of events, believing that the test result had produced enough proof to justify at least moving on to the next stage of the project. True, the force registered had been infinitesimal compared to what I had achieved on countless other occasions. But I blamed that on the lack of time available latterly to get the machine properly tuned. What upset me even more, however, was Dr Davidson's conclusion that in all probability the machine was lifting for no other reason than some weird side-effects created by the motion of the apparatus. I simply couldn't understand how anyone engaged in a research project could dismiss the whole thing in such a high-handed manner without furnishing corroborative evidence. It just wasn't good enough to say what you *think* is happening. Here was a machine that was doing something contrary to known physics. As Professor Laithwaite had said, that demanded an explanation, not a guess.

I said little of all this to Graham Thomson, realizing it was not he who had written out the death sentence. He gave me his best wishes for the future and we parted on a handshake. Within an hour I had cleared my room, packed up my machine and all its accessories, and said my farewells to the lads in the engineering workshop. Then I drove sadly home to tell Janet.

'You're back early today,' she commented, as I came through the back door and sat down at the breakfast bar. I lit a cigarette before answering.

'They've chucked me out,' I said bitterly. 'Cold feet, that's what it is. They've simply run out of bottle.'

When I told her what had transpired in Graham Thomson's office she quickly jumped to my defence. 'They'll rue this day,' she snapped. 'But if that's their attitude you're better out of the place altogether. What you must do now is to go on and prove them wrong.'

I nodded in agreement although I was desperately disappointed that a project in which I had originally placed such hope had now ended in this way.

But the university saga wasn't quite over yet. In the local Dundee *Courier* next day the story of my 'expulsion' dominated the headlines on the main page under the banner: "Flying Saucer" Machine Blow.'

In the report Brian Makin was quoted as saying: 'Our reasons for terminating the agreement are purely financial. We had already put a substantial amount of money into the research and when we considered the progress that had been made, along with the serious financial problems confronting the university, we decided we would be unable to continue sponsoring Mr Kidd's work. We could not foresee any quick results coming from the research and we felt the machine would require a longer term of investigation – perhaps several more months to understand the complex technicalities involved.'

If the professor had stopped at that point I would have licked my wounds and quickly departed without any fuss, even though I considered the university's official reasoning to be unworthy of an intellectual institution. To say you are quitting on a problem after three months because you can't find the answers, particularly when you have laid aside more time for that very function, is plainly ridiculous. To justify that decision on grounds of finance, describing the £8000 spent so far as a 'substantial' investment, was almost laughable.

However, Brian Makin hadn't finished. His statement continued: 'The machine may be able to produce an effect which may be of use in the weightlessness of space, as it does seem to produce a small force on earth which could have a greater effect up there, but I don't think it would be enough to move a flying saucer . . . It seems quite small in relation to the weight of the machine and that is what we call a "second order effect". The moving parts create a lot of vibration and resonance and the lifting effect may be associated with that.'

I was infuriated by all his hedging and speculation with the use of such imprecise terms as 'may', 'could' and 'seem'. To have ventilated his doubts about my machine in public was really inexcusable. At least Ian Davidson had confined his remarks to an internal memo. Fortunately, I had been tipped off about the contents of the professor's criticism and was able to get the right of reply before the newspaper went to press. I summed up my feelings by saying: 'Professor Makin is in no position to pass an opinion on my machine because not once during all the time it had been in his department did he make himself available to watch it being demonstrated. To

72

say it is vibration or any other effect is sheer guesswork and that is not what research is all about. The university has failed to prove anything.'

The following day I held a press conference to put my side of events more fully. The local evening paper, under a four-column headline, spoke about me being 'bloodied but unbowed'. I contended that the university research had lacked thoroughness, then went on: 'I was present during the tests and the university people wanted to conduct the work their way and not mine. They only spent about £8000 on it in four months and as far as I'm concerned they didn't prove or disprove anything. I also feel that Professor Makin's remarks belittle my machine.'

The day after, Scotland's national Sunday newspaper, the *Sunday Mail*, reported that, 'A Scots engineer has baffled the country's top brains with his flying saucer.'

On top of all this Brian Makin sent me a farewell note wishing me all success on the rocky road ahead. He wrote: 'I would advise you that to continue with any further development you should be correctly financed and within an organization which will give you the necessary technical backup. If you are financially successful, then we would consider future development at the university, but you may wish to seek new pastures and I could well understand your views. I know you are so dedicated to your concept and trust that you will one day be successful in convincing the critics one way or the other.'

The professor's valedictory message, although sent in all kindness, only succeeded in adding to my confusion over the university's attitude. The point was that if they had really believed in my machine they could have found the financial backing from an external source to carry on the project. In a scientific book dealing with possible new energy sources in space, published two years later, the author made reference to the university's involvement with my device. He claimed that, 'scepticism and sniping from other academics slowly eroded Dundee University's enthusiasm and they finally pulled the plug on Kidd's gryoscope research.' That was only part of the reason. I have since been told on good authority that my machine was doomed to failure in the university before it even arrived on the campus. When Bill Ferrier breathed his last the research project had, in reality, also died a death at the same time. This theory certainly tied in with the vibes I had picked up during my short stay in the academic world.

However, I want to make it clear in retrospect that I have a certain sympathy for Brian Makin and Ian Davidson in all this. At the time my project was pushed their way they were each busy with their own commitments and couldn't possibly devote the time necessary to undertake properly such a fundamental piece of research as that involved with inertial thrust propulsion. Perhaps, also, I had been unfortunate in going up to the university at the time when its faculties of science and engineering were being restructured and staff were caught up in a ferment of change. There was even some anxiety over security of jobs.

But whatever the contributory causes might have been, I was already preoccupied with other exciting developments. As a result of the Grampian Television documentary which had been transmitted on May 21, just ten days before my sudden and dramatic exit from the university, the story of my machine was now known all over the world. That programme was going to be the most important influence of all in shaping the fortunes of my anti-gravity machine.

Chapter 10

Immediately my entry into Dundee University had been confirmed, just before Christmas 1986, Grampian Television allocated resources to film a half-hour documentary programme which would tell the story of my struggle and determination to build the world's first successful anti-gravity machine. Ron Thompson, who had been hatching out the story for two years, was by then desperately anxious to have the facts publicly known before being 'scooped' by some other reporter finding out about my research project although, ironically, he required the credibility of that project to justify his television programme.

From my own standpoint, I had never hankered after publicity for its own sake as a means of self-aggrandisement. The machine was the thing that mattered most of all and I instinctively knew that if my work was going to be recognized and developed the more people who knew about it the better. Only in that way could other parties who might be interested in backing such an invention as mine find out about the machine's existence. Although I now had a commitment from the university there was no way of knowing how long it would last. I had to keep looking to the future and provide myself with as many options as possible. Publicity was the answer, even at the cost of certain criticism and ridicule for myself and exposure for my family. It was one thing to discuss between ourselves the terrible strains which had been imposed upon our marriage, quite another to bare our souls before a television audience of many millions.

The filming was to be carried out in three stages. The first, at my house in Dundee, would re-enact my work in the shed and garage and describe how it had affected our family life. The next sequence would be filmed at Imperial College, London, where Professor Laithwaite had agreed to participate in restaging my demonstration and evaluate my work. Finally we would go to Dundee University where the programme would report on the progress of the research and hopefully end on a promising note.

When the film crew first arrived at my house in early January, 1987, they knew as little about my work as I knew about theirs. Ron Thompson had wanted to give the programme as low a profile as possible during production to avoid undue curiosity which could inadvertently lead to a leak. No longer could he accuse me of being obsessive about my machine when he had gone almost paranoid about his programme. You can imagine his consternation, therefore, when he discovered that the working title on the film schedules had been given as 'Flying Saucer'. He nearly had apoplexy.

'There's really no harm done,' I said, trying hard to console him. 'With a title like that everyone will think the programme has something to do with fiction.' He admitted later that I had been right. The main reaction had been nods and winks from colleagues who thought it was all some kind of hoax and wanted to book their seats to Mars.

But the film unit soon became wised up on the machine and as the background story unfolded before the camera they were gradually caught up in the excitement of the project. Things, however, got off to a rather embarrassing start. To break me in gently, the director suggested we shoot a mute scene on the beach nearby where I would be filmed showing my granddaughter Nicola how to fly a kite, as I had done as a youngster dreaming one day of building a space ship. As this sequence had been prearranged I made a kite for the occasion. The trouble was it refused to fly properly. After rising to about thirty feet it began to corkscrew and plummet to the ground. I did everything I could to coax it into upper space while everyone hung around shivering in the bitterly cold weather. Eventually the crew managed to patch together a series of shots which, when edited, would make it seem as if the kite had been soaring like a feather. 'Hope your machine turns out to be a better flier than your kite,' joked the cameraman.

Thankfully, everything else went smoothly during that first week of filming. The machine bobbed up and down in the garage while it was shot from every angle and Janet vividly recaptured her memories of the early days. She recalled our courting years spent in the local library where I had read up on Newton and Einstein while she dreamed of the brighter lights. She then moved on to the period when I became a recluse in my shed, so involved with the machine that I could think and talk of nothing else, even in bed. That I can tell you, caused a few hearty laughs later. So did her summing up of life with Sandy

Kidd over the years. 'He just wasn't like a normal person. He never was.'

Janet took to the camera much more naturally than myself. She could speak at ease in front of the lens and never had retakes. I, on the other hand, stumbled and stuttered on many occasions until I overcame my self-consciousness. Professor Eric Laithwaite was different. He is a very able television performer and it was a delight to watch him in action when we eventually moved on to London to film at Imperial College. In fact, he got quite carried away again when he saw the machine repeat its lifting performance during the restaging of the demonstration. Before I realized what was happening, and with the camera still running, he seized my hand in congratulations. 'I think that's fantastic,' he said warmly. 'There cannot be any doubt. There is a whole body that goes up. By whatever means, it goes up.'

In the interview that followed the professor gave a frank and full assessment of both me and my machine. Later in our hotel room Janet and I listened carefully to what he had said in the question and answer session.

Q. Professor, you've been contacted by many people over the years claiming to have invented this and that and, as you know of course, most of them have turned out to be cranks or eccentrics. What was it about Sandy Kidd's first phone call to you that made you believe he was the genuine article?

A. I think mostly his modesty. He didn't make any elaborate claims. He didn't say, 'I've broken Newton's Laws' or anything like that. He described what he had done in more or less the way I would describe it, and you could sense the excitement in his voice. And you think, this man is the one in a hundred, he's different. You do get a sort of a feel for it. You can spot the cranks a mile off. They usually say something terrible in the first five minutes. But Sandy was so obviously genuine and almost self-effacing about what he had done. And, of course, it was gyroscopes and I asked him a few questions such as 'Are they offset gyroscopes with skewed axes?' and 'What does it do?' And he said 'Well, it will lose some of its weight.' At this point you think, I can't afford not to see this because I could be missing a big one. And when he was willing to bring it to me as opposed to me having to go up to

77

the North of Scotland well, of course, he could come and see me. I've got nothing to lose.

Q. So he came to see you. He demonstrated the machine and you saw it work. What was your reaction?

A. I thought, 'He's done it!' It's got the ingredients. He's made a machine out of spare parts. It's crude but he's demonstrated the principles to his own satisfaction and now to mine, and if only he can get this engineered and get some more force out of it then it's up to the Establishment, who say these things can't be done, to explain it some other way, because he's got a machine that loses weight. However else you look at it someone has got to supply the information . . . to supply the explanation by conventional means or accept what I've been saying for years, that, of course, this could be done.

Q. So can you explain to us the significance of what he has achieved so far?

A. Oh yes, without any doubt. You can argue from theory and go to the remotest parts of the universe and start arguing about the origin of the universe but it doesn't mean a thing. You can make theory prove anything you want to. There is no substitute for a man who does it with experiment. It goes right back to Michael Faraday who said, 'All this is a dream. Nothing is too wonderful to be true if consistent with the laws of nature.' And in questions such as these, experiment is the best test of consistency – always experiment. The significance of this is that he did it rather than talking about it, theorizing about it, taking up patents about things that don't work, and so on, wasting money that way. Instead, he got down and did it and has made something that works.

Q. And what exactly is it that he's achieved? What has he done?

A. He's shown that it's possible to convert some angular momentum into some linear momentum and have a reaction.

Q. Is he the first person to have done this?

A. No. Others have done it and inevitably have modified their machines to try to make them better, stopped them from working, and they've never been able to recreate the original machine. I've had several like this that have come along before Sandy and eventually have gone away sadly because they never got their machine to work again.

Q. So how does Sandy Kidd stand?

A. Well, he didn't make the mistake of meddling with his first machine. He kept it, so that when he made a second machine that didn't work he said, 'What's the difference between this and my first machine? It's only the first machine made better.' Then he realized he had lost some of the flexibility through the rather loose engineering of the first machine. He was then able to make a better machine knowing what it is that makes it go. The greatest thing of all is that he's had such perseverance and tenacity, it's unique.

Q. Are you saying then that he really is on the brink of a very big, major breakthrough?

A. Yes. But, of course, so was Michael Faraday. This thing has been going on a long time. Oliver Heaviside predicted it mathematically. It's just that it's never been accepted by the Establishment that this is possible and somehow you need someone like Sandy to bring it into the open and, if I may say, someone like yourselves for putting it on the air so that it makes it public. It makes it known. It gets people talking, then people will come and see his machine, then they'll have to rethink what before was considered dogma, the absolute truth. They'll have to modify it. He's not making claims that Newton's laws are wrong. It's just that you have to be rather careful at how you look at reaction when you're talking about three actions at once, when you're talking about three-dimensional space rather than one-dimensional. Newton's laws are always applied to bodies either travelling in a straight line or rotating round a fixed axis and when there's some of each it's not easy to apply them.

Q. What sort of a person is Sandy Kidd in your estimation – as an engineer and inventor?

A. Oh, he's got what it takes to make an inventor. The French word *ingénieur*, from which the word engineer is derived, means 'an ingenious one' and Sandy is ingenious. There's no question about it.

Q. Why do you say that?

A. You just have to watch the way he works when he gets the counterweight and needs to add extra things. Whereas the conventionalist would put a scale on it and use graded gram weights, Sandy hangs on first of all a metal vice, and that's roughly the right weight. Then he sticks a magnet against it. That gives extra weight and after that he puts four-inch nails against the magnet and keeps piling them on until he gets the right weight. That's making use of the things that are around him. He's got that natural ingenuity that an engineer has. He doesn't have to say, 'Well, I must do it all according to the book.' He looks for the first thing that's available. It's that sort of mentality. It's making use of things.

Q. Do you think he is going to go places?

A. Definitely, because he's got such tenacity, such enthusiasm and such energy and it's not misplaced.

Q. Now, in your endorsement of this machine you spoke about it as having the ingredients of a potential space drive. The implications of that, of course, are absolutely enormous. Are you really saying that what he's got in that machine may some day be the means of revolutionizing space travel?

A. At the moment the only way we know how to propel ourselves through empty space is by shovelling matter out the back in order to go forwards on the shot and gun principle. When we look at the first stage of the rocket you realize just how much fuel you've got to burn, and how fast, simply to get out of the earth's atmosphere. Even after that, to accelerate through space, you must keep using fuel and discharging the effluent out the back. In the end you run out of fuel and for this reason we can only go inwards towards the sun, and not outwards to Saturn and back again. Now, where Sandy's machine differs

80

is that he has produced a force by converting some angular momentum, which is easy to generate with something like a nuclear submarine engine, into linear momentum and if you can do that then you are able to propel your spacecraft forward without the need to push matter out the back. In this way you could go to the next galaxy on a teaspoonful of uranium. There's no question about that. You see, even the science fiction writers have not got this far because in things like 'Star Wars' they have Darth Vadar with his twin ion engines and they're projecting matter out the back at virtually the velocity of light. But if you've got a continuous source of energy as you would with a nuclear engine and you can convert from rotary to linear thrust, then you're free of the rocket for the first time. It's like making a power station without using steam at all.

Q. Does it not surprise you at all that someone like Sandy Kidd, who has no academic qualifications, no advanced grasp of physics and mathematics, someone who is simply a grassroots engineer, has been able to accomplish all this?

A. No. He knows enough physics to keep him going so to speak and he doesn't know enough as to be so brainwashed into believing, like everyone else, that it can't be done. When he believes what he sees with his own eyes, and rightly so, he's liable to latch on to it with everything he's got. He has enough physics to guide him without falling into the pitfalls but not enough to make him hide and say 'Oh, it's no use trying that because the laws say it can't be done.'

Q. This is a very strange alliance in a way. You the great professor, at a seat of learning, and he a humble engineer working in his garden shed in the North of Scotland. It's really quite remarkable the way the two of you have come together and the way you have been able to encourage him and give him a belief in what he has done.

A. Well, it's only because I've been through it several times. I'm playing it low profile at the moment. I can hardly manage another round of that sort of thing. I'll be absolutely certain the next time. He'll soon find out what slings and arrows amount to because I've been through it. He's got to make a bigger machine with faster means and this is going to cost a lot more money. This is when his troubles really begin because then you've got to find someone with enough faith in you to put up the money.

Q. Do you think from what you've seen already in this machine, that the forces he has produced so far can be enhanced and developed and be applied to commercial, industrial and space use?

A. Yes. I'm not sure how far it can be applied but several things are at least highly probable. If you make a thing work then I think it is very highly unlikely that you've made it work in the very best way the first time. In other words, the fact that you've made it work at all means that it can be made to work better and the thing then is – how much better? For example, it would be one thing making a space drive that was useful for going from an orbiting space station outwards into space. But if you first want your machine to go from earth to that orbiting station then it may be worn out by overcoming gravity on the way. That is the big pull. It's really all a question of how well it works now. You know it works, but will it get better if it can be made bigger? There's every reason to have confidence that it will because it's like an induction motor, and that gets better as it gets bigger.

Q. If someone were to ask you to describe Sandy Kidd how would you put it?

A. Oh, he's a great enthusiast. He's an ingenious man who's got a flair for new things and any amount of enthusiasm.

Q. Is he going to be remembered?

A. He'll be rememberd, as I said, if his machine can be multiplied by one hundred and is made that good. Then he'll be remembered.

Q. So it is really quite an exciting time?

A. Oh, I think he is very excited. Yes, indeed. You see I've followed him right through for over a year now because I know he's got something and he knows he's got something and I'm going to help him all I can.

It was rather fascinating listening to myself being analysed in this way, almost like reading your own obituary. It was apparent right through the interview that the professor was treading very warily on the subject of breaking physical laws and who could blame him? He was obviously still smarting from his own experience thirteen years before. In fact, he was being so cautious he was even saying that I was making no claims that Newton was wrong, which, of course, wasn't the case. I firmly believed my machine had broken Newton's Third Law. But I didn't criticize Sir Isaac for that. When he was sitting under the famous apple tree in his parents' garden over three hundred years ago working it all out he certainly wasn't thinking of a device like mine.

But it was the professor's reference to the British physicist Oliver Heaviside (1850–1925) that particularly interested me. Heaviside had said there was an energy flow through space which was not electromagnetic. It was a mechanical spin energy. That being so, it should follow that it was perfectly feasible to create a force by converting angular momentum into linear momentum as demonstrated by my machine. Heaviside had, in fact, predicted the principle on which my device was based.

The following day the professor provided us with more programme material by demonstrating a series of gyro set pieces, using spinning wheels to illustrate the unpredictable way they reacted to certain applied forces, just as I had learned myself through my own experiments in the early days. Again as I watched, I was struck by the way these rotating discs seemed almost to have an intelligence of their own. But the *piéce de résistance* was the professor's huge, cast-iron wheel on a long, heavy axle, very similar to the one I had seen him use with the schoolboy in the television programme in 1974.

He dragged the big, cumbersome contraption across the laboratory floor and heaved it on to a set of scales. 'This thing weighs fifty pounds,' he confirmed, panting from his exertions. 'I'm now going to show you the basic concept of Sandy's machine, how a gyro builds up energy and then uses it to escape from an applied force.' He then asked me to start rotating the gyro with an electric drill which slotted into the centre of the wheel. Within seconds it was spinning at 2000 rpm. The professor, who had previously been straining to hold the gyro just above the floor, now hoisted it easily up to hip level. He then started swinging the enormous object round and round, like the gyros on my machine, until suddenly the huge wheel soared into the air above his head as if it had suddenly lost its weight. 'You just force it to go round a bit faster than you think it can and it goes up in the air,' he commentated with ease, as the wheel floated above him like a halo. 'All on its own. Very little effort required. About as much as lifting an umbrella. No centrifugal force.'

The crew were fascinated by what they had just filmed and several of them later tried out the wheel for themselves to prove that the gyro's behaviour was no illusion.

Everyone was delighted by what had been put into the can at Imperial College. The professor had excelled himself in word and action. Later, while still in London, we recorded a short piece with Martyn Rose in front of the American Embassy in Grosvenor Square, recalling his unsuccessful efforts to raise funding on the other side of the Atlantic. This was the first time I had spoken to him since his final phone call eighteen months previously. He was pleased I had landed a university research project. 'Once you get the machine through a redbrick bastion of respectability it will gain credibility,' he predicted.

Having completed the filming down south, there was no more we could do at that stage. Dundee University was to be the final location but I had only just moved in there and it would be some time yet before we had anything to report. In the meantime, work began on editing the material already shot and to assist in doing this Ron Thompson disappeared for several weeks into a dark room at Grampian's main studios in Aberdeen.

The major problem which now had to be resolved was how to produce a programme with just the right mix of simplified technical data and human interest material for a general audience but one, nevertheless, which would include a large number of engineers and scientists. Achieving this vital balance between information and entertainment with a subject as complex and little understood as gyros was going to be no easy task.

I was particularly anxious that the matter of flying saucers was handled discreetly. I had made a model of one and used it as a prop during my interview while describing how a spacecraft would gather speed by using a gyroscopic propulsion unit. But I felt that to overplay the flying saucer angle could be a form of sensationalism which might lead many viewers to be highly critical of my machine, simply because it was being related to a phenomenon they didn't believe existed. The programme makers agreed. It was suggested that a clip be shown from one of the many feature films depicting flying saucers and life on other planets. But that was regarded as being too dramatic and realistic. Finally the line was drawn by using a montage of photographs of mystery objects in the sky taken by UFO observers in different parts of the world. This sequence was slotted into the top section of the programme where the script referred to the number of people who were convinced that flying saucers were a form of transport used between other planes and the stars and if that was so, their technology was far in advance of anything we were using on earth.

The functioning of my machine, and the way the gyros were creating their lift, was illustrated by a special, animated graphic which took the viewer through every motion in easy stages. Film of Vulcan bombers was used to cover my RAF service and my first unforgettable experience with gyroscopic power. Close-up shots of a launch at Cape Canaveral provided powerful proof of Laithwaite's reference to the present system of space travel being dependent on ejecting massive quantities of processed fuel out the back end of a rocket in order to push forward through the earth's atmosphere.

In the middle of April, by which time Dr Davidson had seen my original machine in full flight, the film unit arrived at the university to complete the shooting. Grampian had by now decided to screen the programme before the end of May, fearing the story might break if they delayed indefinitely, and could therefore wait no longer for the strain gauge tests to be held. These were simulated for the benefit of the camera in the knowledge that they would be completed by the time the programme went out although, of course, no mention could be made of precise measurements. By now the machine was located in a small room in the basement of the engineering block and on the instruction of the University Safety Officer could only be run behind a steel mesh guard. After filming various sequences an interview was recorded with Ian Davidson.

He said that following the strain gauge tests he envisaged more complicated probes in which the forces being generated elsewhere in the machine would also have to be quantified by measuring instruments attached to all the rotating parts. All this preliminary testing might last for several months until they could ascertain the overall behaviour and capability of the device. The interview then continued.

Q. So you are dealing here with something that is pretty complicated?

A. It certainly is a very complicated phenomenon. The dynamics of the system are difficult and it's not at all apparent just by looking at it what is happening, so it will be a bit of time before we can pinpoint the actual mechanism which is creating this force.

Q. Have you ever come across anything like this before?

A. I have not seen anything of this type before. I've never seen a device behaving like this one does.

Q. Does it excite you?

A. Yes, I find it very exciting. I would very much like to track down what is really happening.

Q. How promising do you really find it at the end of the day in giving us a new source of prime energy?

A. Well, I would prefer to answer that question some time later when I have a much clearer picture of what the machine actually does and the extent of this. At the moment it is an interesting phenomenon. Let's examine it and see what comes from it.

Q. Could it be big?

A. My initial reaction would be, probably not. But unless we can really understand the basic mechanism then we can't really predict the likely size.

Q. How difficult is it going to be working out the mathematics of a thing like this?

A. That I would imagine is a fairly extensive problem. It's a difficult problem. I would have thought it's the sort of thing that we might well contemplate as a research project for a three-year Ph.D. or something of that nature.

Q. As interesting as that?

A. I would say so, yes.

Q. Is it within the present world of dynamics?

A. Yes, it must be. The question is simply whether we can set up the correct mathematical model. This is usually the problem if a phenomenon doesn't obey the mathematics. It's usually the mathematics that are wrong and we certainly have to keep extending that until we get the two to agree with each other.

Q. Now, you are a dyed-in-the-wool academic. Do you have an open mind on this?

A. Yes. The longer I'm about dynamics the less I'm prepared to say it can't happen. I would like to learn a lot more about it.

Q. What do you think of Sandy Kidd?

A. He is a man of considerable determination. He's pushed the project on as I understand it for a number of years and he's produced a device which behaves in an interesting fashion.

Although Ian Davidson had been more restrained in his optimism than Eric Laithwaite, I was perfectly happy with his evaluation of the machine at that stage. It was intriguing to think that according to him I had developed an engineering phenomenon in a garden shed which had produced a mathematical problem interesting enough for a research thesis. Everything he had said during this interview I was later to compare with his curt dismissal of my project in his final report to the Industrial Liaison Department. Why had he altered his opinion so drastically?

When the programme had been finally edited and all the

sound tracks added, Janet and I were given a special preview. The title eventually chosen was, 'The Man Who Wants to Change the World', a play on the phrase I had originally used in my first phone call to Ron Thompson when I told him my machine was going to do precisely that. The documentary opened with me walking from my house to the garage and throwing open the door to reveal the machine standing alone in the middle of the floor as the first strains of the haunting, space-like theme music filtered through. The impact was certainly impressive, creating an atmosphere full of mystery. The programme ended with me looking confidently to the future and predicting that the 'academic chappies' would eventually have to come round to my way of thinking. Then finally the words of the famous Russian scientist and writer Immanuel Velikovsky came rolling up the screen. 'What I have to impress upon you is that science today, as in the days of Newton, lies before us as a great uncharted ocean, and we have not yet sailed very far from the coast of ignorance.'

We were both pleased and relieved at the way the programme had been put together. It was not sensational in any way; simply the story of how an ordinary suburban family had found themselves falling under the influence of a strange machine. As we sat and watched the programme alone in our lounge, Janet and I found it difficult to believe that all this had happened to us.

The transmission date was fixed for May 21, 1987. Initially the programme would only be seen by Grampian's million and a quarter viewers in an area stretching from mid-Scotland, north to the Shetlands and west to the Hebrides. Normally the company would have mounted a publicity exercise beforehand giving details of what the documentary was all about. With this one, however, they were unable to disclose too much advance information because it was an exclusive story. What they did was to publicize a picture of myself standing beside the machine with a caption saying this was the Dundee engineer who had invented a device which he claimed was going to open up the universe.

The programme was being shown at seven in the evening. I sat staring at the clock as the hands moved round to the witching hour. It was a strange feeling to realize that very shortly now the privacy of my family life was going to be blown wide open. I was about to take another step into the unknown.

Chapter 11

In the days following the screening of the programme Janet and I were nearly swept off our feet by a wave of publicity and public response. Reporters and photographers descended upon the house in droves. The telephone never stopped ringing with calls from home and abroad. Strangers kept stopping us in the street. The popular press gave national coverage to the story and pictures, with the item being lifted out of their foreign editions by other papers in many parts of the world.

Headlines everywhere, it seemed, were screaming out the news. The *Daily Mail* proclaimed: 'Eureka! The Garden Shed Secret of a Magnificent Man and His Flying Machine'; *Daily Express*: 'Sandy's Invention Out of This World'; *Daily Star*: 'Wife Over the Moon!'. Scotland's own national and local press also gave the story splash treatment. The tabloids, in particular, really went to town. For them, the story of an amateur inventor emerging from his garden shed with a space machine which baffled the scientists was a fairytale come true. They paid scant attention to the possibility of vibration, friction, or any other sort of secondary effect. Professor Laithwaite's word was good enough for them. Bill Ferrier's, too, just before he died. And there was Professor Stephen Salter repeating his Nobel Prize prediction, made so dramatically at the demonstration in Edinburgh University.

It was also interesting to observe the way the press handled the flying saucer aspect of the story. Whereas the television programme had adopted a cautious approach, the popular papers suffered from no such inhibition. They shouted the phrase from the roof-tops. Indeed, according to one paper I had invented the flying saucer and in a follow-up feature in the *Daily Express*, describing how the machine had nearly wrecked my marriage, they actually had a drawing of a saucer hovering over the headline. In all this coverage, however, the serious broadsheets had preferred to remain aloof. They had not been interested in carrying the story. Ron Thompson spoke to the science correspondent of one of the 'heavies' but was told the machine couldn't possibly be genuine because it didn't comply with physics. Oh, these lofty experts passing judgements in their writing garrets. Only *The Times* deigned to get off its perch several days after the story broke with a report by their transport correspondent. He compared my machine to the gyroscopic device of a Swindon physics teacher, Peter Greed, who had taken out a patent in 1974. Laithwaite was quoted as saying: 'What Mr Kidd has achieved so far he has achieved by pure intuition. I want to see what more his intuition can turn up. He might just turn up something that the experts miss. We need all the help we can get.'

Although I had braced myself for a certain reaction to the television documentary, the scale of the publicity caught me totally unawares and I was unprepared for the volume of letters and phone calls it brought to my house. Everyone, it seemed, had been thinking of a machine like mine for years and what a coincidence it was that I had now actually built one. Many of these correspondents sent me detailed drawings of what their device would look like. Several who were working on serious projects similar to mine, including an inventor in Winnipeg, Canada, were anxious to pool resources and collaborate on a joint machine. There was also no shortage of theories as to how my device actually produced its thrust, from the most complicated explanations right down to the lady who wondered if the answer lay in the volume of compressed air created by the gyros' rotation. She wrote: 'My reason for such an observation is that I had an old spin-drier a couple of years ago and found that by putting two dry bath towels into it when switched on, the whole machine became airborne, moving vertically upwards, and I wondered at that time if this could be the means of powering flying saucers.'

Another enthusiast, who confessed he was no scientist but a deep thinker, thought my machine could be utilizing an unknown source of energy in the atmosphere and for that reason he felt no testing equipment could be properly tuned in to analyse the force it was producing. 'In a sense your device is operating on a higher octave than anything presently known to man,' he concluded.

Among the many writers who just wanted to pat me on the back and wish me luck was a retired advertising agent in the Manchester area who explained how he had recently dreamed of being given a conducted tour of a 'strange flying vehicle' which was powered by an arrangement of gyroscopes similar in design to my machine. He described the layout of the propulsion unit in great detail. This abstract experience he felt was a good omen for the future of my project. There were also requests from schools, colleges and universities for more detailed information about the machine. A degree student at a polytechnic actually wanted to recreate my device and run his own experiments on it as his final year project.

Letters were addressed to me in all sorts of ways. One envelope simply said: 'Sandy Kidd, Gyroscopic Propulsion Genius, Dundee.' There were, of course, one or two on a sour note from people who dismissed the whole idea as a nonsense. From Chichester in Sussex a chartered engineer, who had made a special study of ships' propulsion without the use of external devices such as propellers, wrote to Dundee University expressing his astonishment over the research project. According to the story he had read about me ' . . . gyroscopic propulsion had been invented again. I find it hard to believe that a university engineering department is taking this matter seriously.'

From all this response there was absolutely no doubt the story had captured the public imagination in a very positive way. It was a subject which seemingly occupied the thoughts of countless people, most of them frustrated at not having the wherewithal to become actively involved themselves. An electrical engineer in Colne, Lancashire, told me: 'I look at the newspaper photograph of your machine every day. I simply cannot get it out of my mind. It is beginning to haunt me.'

Many people were already regarding me as a hero, the man who was going to turn fiction into fact by making exploration of the universe a possibility; the inventor who had overcome huge odds at great personal sacrifice to give mankind a new vision of the way ahead. There were two tangible examples of recognition arising from the emotional reaction to what I had achieved so far. At that time a new musical was being performed at a suburban arts festival in Edinburgh. The action centred round three women who attempt to blow up a housing scheme without injuring the inhabitants, but finish up by killing themselves. God then sends them back to earth by means of an umbrella-controlled time machine. At the point in the script where they complained to God's engineering angel that he was not getting them back fast enough the producer worked in a reference to my project by having the angel reply: 'Hang on a minute. I'm not Sandy Kidd you know.' To which the women responded:

'And who is Sandy Kidd?' The angel replied: 'Ah, you won't have heard of him. He's not dead yet.' The producer wrote to me proudly: 'It is the first theatrical production to make reference to your historic achievement.'

The second compliment was paid to me by the management of a new visitor centre in central Scotland. The centre's theme was 'Great Scots'. Here they portrayed the achievements of such famous Scottish figures as television pioneer John Logie Baird, Alexander Graham Bell, the inventor of the telephone, James Watt, whose perfection of the steam engine did so much to usher in the Industrial Revolution, and James Clerk Maxwell, regarded as second only to Einstein and Newton in the history of science. Here you could trace the developments of such famous Scottish products as marmalade, postage stamps, the vacuum flask and a host of other inventions which have been given to the world by a nation of only five million people.

Now they decided to introduce a section looking to the future of Scottish innovation. They erected a big cut-out of a flying saucer with flashing lights against a background of the universe. A picture of me and my machine was placed alongside with an explanatory panel which read: 'Flying saucers haven't been invented yet, at least not on this planet, but when they are it could well be someone like Sandy Kidd whose ingenuity, in the true sense of Scottish innovation, finally unlocks the secrets of the universe. This Edinburgh-born engineer, now living in Dundee, has invented a gyroscopic propulsion unit for a spacecraft which would streak across the heavens to take man where he has never gone before.'

This was all good, romantic stuff in the classic tradition of adventure fiction and although I was greatly touched by all the flattery and adulation, it was still very premature coming at such an early stage of our research. It was rather like tempting Providence. No sooner had I thought so when the university suddenly ended the project and the bottom seemed to fall out of my world.

My main concern now, of course, was to find another backer. I simply couldn't afford to let the trail go dead. But I need not have worried on that score. The widespread publicity had done its job well and soon brought other interested parties knocking on my door. Within days I had been invited to Edinburgh for talks with senior executives of a merchant bank who were exploring the feasibility of investing up to half a million pounds into the research of my machine, with untold funds being available for commercial exploitation.

A consortium of businessmen in central Scotland, who had been following my progress through the university, now also made me a concrete offer. They were prepared to invest up to £100,000 in exploring the machine's potential over a twelve-month period, for which I would draw a salary of £24,000. In exchange for this, I would transfer my rights to the development to a limited company for fifty per cent of its share capital. Of the remaining shares, forty-five per cent would be held by the consortium with the five per cent balance being issued to future investors 'at a hopefully high premium.'

From the owner of a South African engineering company in the Transvaal there came a letter and several phone calls pressing me to accept his financial backing for a research project. 'I would love to get involved financially and also in a "hands on" way with your invention,' he wrote, on reading my story in his local newspaper.

Yet another enquiry arrived from the Advanced Energy Research Institute in London. This was a privately funded body seeking new energy sources by acting as a catalyst in raising funds for projects such as mine which involved radical innovation and new technology on the frontiers of science. Its chairman was Sir Ian MacGregor, former head of British Steel and the National Coal Board, and now a non-executive director of Lazards Bank. He called for a tape of the programme. At the same time a request for talks was made by the chief executive of a micro-light aircraft company in the English Midlands.

In the midst of all this negotiating activity there was a phone call from the British manager of an Australian company called BWN Industries. He explained that their top man had heard about my machine in Melbourne and, as he was planning to be in the United Kingdom shortly, would like to meet me and discuss sponsorship. He would be willing to come to Dundee. A meeting was fixed in a city hotel for the evening of June 12, the day following the 1987 general election. There was no further contact from the company and no letter confirming the meeting. I knew nothing more about them than their name. Nevertheless, I decided not to take a final decision on any of the other propositions until hearing what the Australians had in mind.

As the day of the meeting grew nearer I was convinced that another phone call would arrive out of the blue cancelling the meeting. But none came. On the appointed night I picked up

Ron Thompson and drove into the city for my rendezvous with the mystery men from the other side of the world. 'I'm almost willing to bet no one will turn up,' I remarked pessimistically, as the hotel came into view.

'Can't see it myself,' replied Ron. 'Much too casual an arrangement for my liking.'

My expectations were rock bottom as I pushed my way through the swing doors into the hotel lobby.

'Sandy Kidd?' The unmistakable twang in the voice turned my head sharply towards an alcove below the main stairway. Rising from a table and striding towards me with outstretched hand was a stocky man of medium height and open, smiling face. 'Noel Carroll of BWN,' he announced with a firm handshake. 'Pleased to meet you Sandy. Come and meet the others.' At the table were his financial manager from Melbourne and his British manager from Gloucester.

As we sat down he explained they had just driven up from Birmingham after business there that morning. 'Long day you've had,' I murmured, now embarrassed by the odds I had been offering against his appearance.

'Well, that's how it is, Sandy,' explained Carroll, in an instantly chummy way. 'I'm in high technology. Must keep moving to keep up with things. I jump about all over the place. Round the world several times a year in fact.'

He spoke in short, staccato sentences and had a restless demeanour. I could tell already he was a highly charged, up-and-go individual. His bright, friendly eyes never left my face as he carefully weighed me up and I could tell he was now impatient to get down to business. He didn't seem interested in small talk.

'How did you find out about my machine?' I asked as a means of breaking into the subject.

'Well, Sandy, you'll hardly believe this,' he said, with a quick laugh, 'but I'm driving through Melbourne listening to a local station on my car radio when I pick up this report about a guy at Dundee University in Scotland who's working on this new type of space machine. I nearly ran off the road in surprise. Sort of thing I'm very interested in. We have a number of different research projects on the go at the moment. So I got on the blower right away to Gloucester and told them to fix up a meeting. What d'ye make of that Sandy?'

I shook my head in disbelief. 'People have been picking up the story all over the place but that takes the biscuit.'

Later I discovered that a freelance journalist in Kent taped a weekly report on UK news for one of Melbourne's local radio stations, 3AW. He had read my story in the national press and included it as one of his items.

'Do you want to start by looking at the television programme?' I asked. 'That gives you all the background.' Carroll promptly agreed and we all bundled into his manager's Daimler and drove to the Grampian studio where Thompson had set up a tape for such a contingency. During the short journey I updated the story by explaining what had happened at the university. At the studio the visitors watched the programme in silence.

'How do you see the next stage, Sandy?' asked Carroll before the end titles had even left the screen.

I had been warned that Australians didn't mince their words so I decided to be equally forthright. 'I need time, money and other people's help in building a better machine to give improved performance,' I replied. 'I have talks going at the moment with several other parties including a bank.'

He raised his eyebrows. 'A bank?' he repeated. 'They'll be after their pound of flesh with their interest charges. You can bet your bottom dollar on that. Made up your mind on anything yet?'

'No. I've been waiting on you before deciding what to do next.'

He seemed pleased. 'Can I see the machine?'

I told him he was welcome to examine it in the garage although it wasn't set up to go. Within minutes we were back in the Daimler heading for the house. After a quick hello to Janet in the lounge we headed out the back door to the garage.

'So this is it,' mused Carroll, circling the machine slowly before dropping on his haunches to get a closer look at its mechanism. For the next fifteen minutes I answered all his questions on the technical nature of the device, describing every stage I had gone through before finally getting the breakthrough.

'You've got great faith in this, haven't you?' he asked finally.

'It's the real thing,' I said. 'I'd bet my life on it.'

He nodded and looked at his watch. 'Ten o'clock,' he announced. 'Time we discussed all this over a meal.'

I slipped back into the house to book a table at a local restaurant. 'Who are they?' Janet asked urgently.

'Don't quite know yet,' I replied hurriedly, picking up the phone. 'They're in high technology of some sort. I'll find out later.'

The following two hours passed like some sort of dream. Even today I have to pinch myself and ask whether it all really happened. But it did.

Seated round the restaurant table Noel Carroll explained that he and his brothers Bob and William had formed their own business in 1967 and called it BWN after the initials of their first names. They had originally built their fortune on automatic opening doors by capturing a huge slice of the world market with a novel design of microwave sensor to activate the doors instead of the usual pressure pads. Their next big break came in the early 1980s when they seized on the commercial possibilities of a new type of oilfield technology which had been pioneered in the laboratories of Southampton University. A research team there had designed a hydrocyclone for the separation of oil and water, the first time that liquids had been effectively isolated in this way. With BWN at the helm, six million dollars was spent over three years developing the project into a viable commercial product called the Vortoil. By providing a more effective and economical way of dealing with high water content in oil, this latest process would increase production in off-shore fields while at the same time meeting stringent environmental standards at sea. This separator plant went on to win world-wide sales, escalating to fifty million dollars by 1988.

Noel Carroll was obviously the whizz kid behind all this enterprise. I soon gathered that he prided himself on his ability to spot a winner at a great distance and turn it into a money machine. At the present time he was funding various research projects in the scientific field and was particularly interested in alternative forms of energy. At the age of thirty-nine he had become one of Australia's leading entrepreneurs. His company now had plants in Australia, New Zealand, America, Britain, and a joint venture in Saudi Arabia.

Carroll, with his rapid, shorthand type of delivery, had explained all this to me by the time we had finished our soup. It was during the main course that he completely bowled me over. Suddenly, without any preamble, he stopped eating and leaned across the table. 'Sandy, I've made up my mind,' he said briskly. 'I want you to come and develop your machine with us. How d'ye feel about that?'

I gazed at him in astonishment. 'But . . . but,' I stammered. 'You haven't even seen the machine work yet or spoken to anyone about it. I – .'

'Never mind all that,' he interrupted impatiently. 'I've met you, seen your machine and watched the television programme. I know

96

enough. I have a feeling about this thing. It could be big. Really big. If it is I want to be there. What d'ye say, Sandy?'

By now my mind was in turmoil. Janet simply wasn't going to believe this. 'Where would all this take place?' I asked eventually.

'Anywhere you like. Australia, America or Scotland. Makes no difference to me.'

Again I lapsed into silence. The others had not spoken a word.

'Tell you what, Sandy,' said Carroll. 'Why don't you let us fly you and your wife out to Australia where you can see our set up for yourself and then decide whether you want to join us. Will you do that?'

I couldn't prevent myself smiling at his boyish enthusiasm. 'When would that be?' I asked incredulously.

He consulted his diary. 'I'll be back in Melbourne in a couple of weeks. Let's make it then. In the meantime you go home and discuss all this with your wife. John, here, will be in touch in a couple of days to make all the arrangements.'

A few minutes later he and the others were on their way to stay overnight in Edinburgh, before flying out to America the following day by Concorde. When I got home at midnight Janet was still up. 'Well, what's happening?' she demanded, before I had even time to shut the front door.

I decided to play it cool. 'Nothing much,' I said, walking into the lounge and stretching myself out on one of the chairs.

'Come on, Sandy, tell me the truth,' she demanded, following close on my heels.

'Well, the truth is that we're off to Australia.'

Janet glared at me for several seconds. Then pointing her finger at me accusingly she thundered, 'Sandy Kidd. You've been drinking!'

Chapter 12

Even at this early stage, with so much still to discuss and decide, the Australian intervention was an exciting prospect. The way in which these businessmen had stormed in and out of Dundee that evening, like some sort of raiding party from the outback, had certainly been unorthodox. If someone had asked me to produce written evidence of their offer, or even that such a meeting had ever taken place at all, I could not have furnished the proof.

But I had already formed a favourable impression of Noel Carroll. I had been dealing with people long enough in industry to form judgement of character and I could tell he was not a fly-by-night who had simply been after as much technical data about my machine as he could get on the pretence of being a possible backer. He was obviously the boss of his outfit, able to take decisions on the spot without having to hold committee meetings. The comparative silence of his entourage had borne that out. He was a man who played hunches. He didn't mess about with formality or protocol. If all this was true, and I believed it was, then his intentions about my machine were both genuine and serious.

Janet, however, remained sceptical. Like me she had been disillusioned and disappointed over the outcome of the university project and was now a bit pessimistic about the future. She felt the Australian offer was too good to be true and we would hear nothing more about it. But just as I had been proved wrong in thinking they would never turn up in Dundee, so was she now going to be just as far off the mark with her prediction. Four days later BWN's British manager phoned to ask if we had decided to make the 'red carpet' reconnaissance trip down under. I said we would be pleased to go. Strictly speaking this was only true as far as I was concerned. Janet had a great fear of flying and had sworn never to go in an aeroplane. I was hoping that she would change her mind as details of the trip became known. I was delighted, therefore, to be told that we would be staying in Los Angeles for several days on the way out to familiarize ourselves with the company's American operation and to visit all the famous tourist attractions. We would then wing our way across the Pacific to Australia. The flights would be all luxury class and we would stay in the best hotels. The manager sounded like one of these people who come on the phone to break the news that you've just won a fabulous holiday trip for two. But it was only when our flight tickets duly arrived that Janet finally relented. This, she decided, was simply too big an experience to miss. Even though it was going to be a 'white knuckle' job all the way to Melbourne and back, she was going to go through with it. As she said herself, the luxury would help.

From the moment we flew out of London in the last week of June we were given constant VIP treatment both in the air and on the ground. It was a lifestyle we had never tasted before. Our previous trips abroad had been confined to occasional overland holidays to European destinations. But this was in a totally different league. This was the way the other half lived. Janet so enjoyed the in-flight pampering as an ambassador-class passenger, the champagne and smoked salmon, the eye pads and the slippers, that the ten-hour flight to Los Angeles passed as a dream and not the nightmare she had been dreading. California, too, we soon discovered was the land of gracious living. No wonder they call it the Golden State, the place where people dream of settling. We were met by a limousine and whisked out to the company's plant in the Pasadena area where they made automatic doors and assembled the oily water separators. Here we met Noel's two brothers Bob and Bill who looked after the American end of the business. They immediately made us feel at home and I was able to brief them personally on my work. Bob, being the more technically minded of the two, was particularly fascinated by what I had achieved so far with force-precessed gyros and I could sense that wherever I finished up developing my new machine he would be taking a close interest.

During our four-day stay in Los Angeles we took in Hollywood and Disneyland and marvelled at the magnificent beaches and townships edging the ocean for as far as the eye could see. Our postcards home were filled with the awe and wonder of it all. Then we were on our way round the world to Melbourne where once again the good life awaited us by courtesy of BWN. Here we were installed in the city's newest hotel, the Hyatt in Collins Street, a pink marbled palace of mind-boggling luxury which had only been opened the previous year. Our room on the twenty-ninth floor gave us a panoramic view of a charming city with its tree-lined streets and colourful trams. Noel Carroll was determined we were going to get a good impression of this land of opportunity and over the next ten days we were treated like visiting royalty.

Noel we soon discovered had a weakness for cars of the finest pedigree. His personal fleet consisted of a Rolls Corniche, the latest Bentley, a Jaguar and a Mercedes. Each day he picked us up at the hotel in one of his gleaming chariots and took us off on another stage of our great adventure. We visited the top clubs and the best restaurants. We met his wife and young family at their mansion house set in the famous Dandenong Hills, fifty miles from Melbourne. Standing in a twenty-acre estate cut out of a mountain ash forest, the house was surrounded by an outside swimming pool with sliding roof, a recreational block with a gymnasium and squash courts, tennis courts with pavilion, and five lakes, each one cascading into the other as the ground sloped away from the front of the complex. Later we went down the coast from Melbourne to Noel's beach house at Port Sea and there we sailed in his ocean-going cabin cruiser in warm waters so far from home.

There was, of course, important business to discuss and this occupied much of our time. BWN's headquarters were actually in Dandenong itself, a sprawling commercial town which is not particularly attractive but enjoys the glorious hinterland of the Dandenong Hills. The firm had their factories and offices on a technology estate only a short distance from the town centre and here I was shown the workshop facilities I would be using to build my new machine. By now it had been assumed by Noel Carroll that I would be working in Australia, although my country of destination had been left open-ended at our initial talks in Dundee. I had no objection to settling for a spell in Australia. I liked the relaxed and informal atmosphere of the country and its people and when we were told that a house would be provided Janet, too, became enthusiastic about the prospect. Indeed, after only five days in Melbourne I decided to forget about the other possible funding options still hanging fire at home and to go for an Australian deal. It made sense. BWN was an ambitious, high technology company with considerable financial muscle, led by a forward-looking, self-made man who had faith in what I was trying to achieve. My project would fit comfortably into such an environment. Besides which, a spell of living in a country with such a glamorous outdoor image, and a culture reflecting the traditions of both Britain and America, also had its attractions. It was now up to the company to come up with a reasonable package of proposals.

A number of meetings were held in the city with BWN's solicitors and patent attorneys. The patent experts studied the Dundee University application and drawings and, naturally enough, were sceptical that such a machine could produce the forces being claimed. But, on the other hand, they were impressed by the testimonials of those who had seen it work. In any case, like their counterparts in Scotland, their task was not to pass judgement but to present a case for the machine which would satisfy the conditions laid down in patent law.

While the patent attorneys were dissecting the British patent application, the solicitors were drawing up a Heads of Agreement for a proposed joint venture. This would consist of two separate companies, each with its own equity and field of responsibility, with myself, Noel Carroll and his brother Bob as the directors of both. The first company to be formed would research and develop the new machine in a proving phase lasting not less than six months. If the machine was successfully proved as a mechanical device capable of exerting thrust without a reaction, a second company would be set up to cover the commercialization phase. At that stage both companies would devise a business plan to build an industrial prototype and 'to plan and plot the future commercial exploitation of the process and associated equipment.' It would be the task of the commercial company to 'manufacture, market, sell and distribute the process under exclusive worldwide licence.' At the same time the research branch would continue its development work in order to open up more markets with further commercial applications. My contract would be for a minimum period of six months to cover the proving phase. After that my machine and I would be judged on merit.

The agreement was entirely subject to Dundee University assigning their share of the patent rights to BWN so that the Australian company could assume the priority date on which the application, in both our names, had been filed. Unless they could take over the university's precedence in this way, a fresh application by the Australians at a later date could be invalidated in the event of another inventor having applied for a similar patent in the meantime. It was, therefore, vital that such a transfer took place. BWN was prepared to pay the university the £8000 they had expended over my project and, in a letter I had previously received from the Industrial Liaison Department, these were the terms under which they said they would be prepared to assign their share of the patent rights. The way ahead seemed clear. Janet and I held a family conference in our hotel room, linked up by telephone to our daughters back home, and the decision was taken to sign a letter of intent with BWN and have the agreement vetted later by my own solicitor in Dundee before signing the formal contract.

The negotiations had been conducted in an amicable atmosphere and all those taking part had signed confidentiality agreements to protect the sensitive nature of the technical information involved. Noel Carroll, with all his experience in research and development, was very security minded and had insisted on these precautionary steps being taken. This secrecy measure, however, would not prevent me from engaging in the sort of general publicity with which I had already been involved. Ron Thompson and I had kept in daily touch since I had arrived in Melbourne and a couple of days before leaving for home he decided to break the story of the Australian project. Grampian constructed a graphic tracing my journey across the world and Ron recorded a telephone interview with me as I sat in my hotel bedroom at midnight. The following day the newspaper headlines in Scotland announced: 'Inventor's Amazing Offer from Australia'. The story described how the company, whose name and exact location I had promised to conceal at this stage, had spent £10,000 on flying Janet and I out to Australia via California on a no-expenses-spared trip for financial talks on the future of my anti-gravity machine.

We arrived back in Dundee after an unforgettable seventeen-day trip, tired but elated. Now it was a case of waiting until the agreement was legally finalized before we headed back down under. While the solicitors in Dundee and Melbourne negotiated over changes in various clauses, I went back to the drawing board to design my next machine, prototype Mark 5, which would be built in a land far removed from my garden shed. Then suddenly in that summer of 1987, while we quietly prepared for our temporary emigration to Australia, I was caught up at the centre of a blazing row over the 'brain drain'.

It started quietly enough in the correspondence columns of the local newspaper. It finished up at Cabinet level within the government. The letter which sparked off the controversy had been written and signed by Michael Marra of Newtyle, a small country town ten miles from Dundee. It read:

'If Dundee inventor Sandy Kidd's project leaves this country we can all be thoroughly ashamed of ourselves. It is distasteful enough to read in your columns of the pathetic carpings and betting shop mentality of visionless men, let alone entertaining the thought of Australians cracking jokes about a Scottish university – in the City of Discovery – declaring they've spent £7987.75 and there's still no sign of the nearest galaxy. The professor involved could make clear to the government his outrage at not being able to function properly without appropriate funding by resigning in protest at not being able to play his part in history.'

Shortly after, Mr Marra called at my house and introduced himself as the correspondent. He said he was a professional musician and had written a song in protest at the way I had been forced to seek financial help abroad. Entitled 'Australia Instead of the Stars', and sung to a melancholic air, the fourth and final verse proclaimed:

And in this wilderness of downward thumbs
Until we've done our homework there will be worse to come
Now we've spent the eight thousand
Such an unhappy sound
And we don't know the stars from a hole in the ground
We'll get by selling cars
We know what we are

When he said he would be singing the number at various concerts throughout Scotland I didn't really take him too seriously. Mind you, I had never had anyone knock on my door before and tell me they had written a song in my honour. Then several weeks later I tuned in to a BBC Scotland radio programme called 'Travelling Folk' which had been recorded at the Edinburgh Festival. I nearly fell off my chair when I suddenly heard Michael Marra introduce my song, explain what it was all about, then sing it with great gusto.

But things really came to a head towards the end of August when Janet and I were given a civic farewell by the Lord Provost of Dundee at a small private reception in his parlour, days before leaving again for Australia. There was, of course, a terrible irony about this gesture of goodwill. Dundee had not long adopted the symbol 'City of Discovery' inspired by the return to her native city of Captain Scott's famous ship *Discovery* which had taken the explorer on his expedition to the South Pole at the turn of the century. The historic vessel, built in Dundee and latterly languishing in London Docks, had now become the rallying point for the attraction of new industry and the creation of fresh prosperity in the city. But many observers believed that Dundee, in allowing me to leave, was now waving goodbye to the very sort of innovation it was trying to attract within its boundaries.

All these happenings, however, had not gone unnoticed by my local MP John McAllion, who issued a statement saying he was to complain officially to the government about the way in which my invention had been 'snatched' from under Scottish noses by a company on the other side of the world. He wrote first to the Secretary of State for Scotland, Mr Malcolm Rifkind. The letter read:

> Please find enclosed background information dealing with the case of my constituent, Mr Sandy Kidd, who is developing a revolutionary machine for converting rotary into linear motion. There are a number of points of concern arising out of the circumstances in which Mr Kidd's machine is now to be developed in Australia rather than here in Scotland. Firstly, how can it be that Scottish-based innovatory research of this kind can be snatched from under our noses by a company on the other side of the world? This was a project which had distinguished academic backing. It had been taken on by Dundee University as a research project but had to be abandoned for reasons which, according to the university's head of mechanical engineering, were "purely financial". The Scottish Development Agency had looked at the project and expressed an interest, yet failed to act to ensure funding which would have retained the project in Scotland. The Scottish financial sector, too, had received approaches to provide funding, but again failed to respond to these proposals in sufficient time to keep the project here. It is obviously too late now, in the case of Mr Kidd's project, to repair the damage. However, it is quite appalling that innovatory work of this kind should have been lost to Scotland through lack of response on the part of the different agencies mentioned above and I would ask that, as a matter of urgency, you take the necessary steps to ensure that the appropriate lessons are drawn from this unfortunate incident. There is clearly a lack of adequate funding for research in Scottish universities otherwise Dundee would not have been

forced to abandon this project. How do you propose to remedy this lack of funding? Further, the SDA and the financial sector in Scotland have clearly failed to act decisively and speedily in this instance. How do you intend to act to ensure that this failing is not repeated? We can all pay lip service to the need to back innovatory research with the necessary funding to ensure that it is developed and commercially exploited in our own country. But it will only be lip service as long as innovators such as Mr Kidd are forced to join the brain drain in order to develop their work. I look forward to receiving your comments on this matter.

This letter was followed by a second complaint ten days later, this time addressed to Kenneth Baker, Secretary of State for Education and Science, and one of the government's senior ministers. This letter, written under the heading of 'Government Support for Science and Technology', was equally critical of government policy:

I write to you on the above matter following the particular case of an inventor from Dundee, Mr Sandy Kidd, who has devised a so-called 'outer gravity' machine. Mr Kidd's creation received little or no note from agencies in Scotland and the device is now being developed in Australia. This is yet another example of government failure to support and encourage scientific and technological innovation in this country. You will be aware that the DTI's Technology Requirements Board has just published a report saying that if Britain is to survive in the modern technological world the government must first double its financial support for industrial research and development. In July the Royal Society expressed concern at the 'continued emigration of talented scientists and engineers from the UK' caused by reduced UK funding for research and increased investment in research in other countries. I would strongly urge your department to take note of such observations, and the experience of Mr Kidd, and increase substantially government support in such fields. I have written to the Scottish Office on the lack of support shown towards Mr Kidd's invention.

At the time these letters were written the Press asked me for my reaction. I said that developments were going abroad all the time and if Britain was going to invest in the future it would have to back the

105

achievements of its own people. I added: 'I agree with Mr McAllion's decision to raise the matter with the Scottish Secretary – someone definitely had to do it. Given the choice, I would have preferred to develop my invention in Dundee but I was realistic enough to see it wasn't to be. I would still hope to be able to involve Dundee in the development of the machine at some stage.'

Replying on behalf of the Scottish Secretary, Mr Ian Lang, the Minister of State at the Scottish Office with special responsibility for industry, sent Mr McAllion the following reply:

Thank you for your letter to the Secretary of State in which you draw his attention to the difficulties faced by your constituent, Mr Sandy Kidd, in his attempts to develop his machine. Naturally I share your desire to retain and exploit our native inventiveness to the benefit of Scottish industry and the Scottish economy, just as I am equally concerned to increase the level of innovation within our indigenous companies. By the same token it is of the greatest importance that both research and development resources, whether in the public or private sector, are devoted to work that has a real prospect of success. Mr Kidd's claims for his device imply that Newton's Laws of Motion, which have served mankind well for three centuries, are in serious error. Such claims clearly require exceptionally rigorous appraisal and demonstrated replicability before they can be accepted by the scientific community. I understand that the work that was carried out at Dundee University did not provide such support for Mr Kidd's claims, and that the people involved felt that the likelihood of obtaining such support was so remote as not to justify further expenditure. In these circumstances it comes as no surprise to me that the financial institutions in Britain also decided not to fund development. So far as the Agency is concerned, I am informed that no direct approach was made to them. Had it been, they also would not have provided funding, for their interests are primarily in promoting commercial ventures rather than in supporting original research. Although I cannot be more encouraging on this specific case, I can assure you that this government is committed to raising the technological awareness and innovative capability of our indigenous industries and, as part of this campaign, we are committing very large sums of money to support the establishment and expansion of technical centres of excellence within our major universities and central institutions: you will no doubt be aware, for example, that Dundee University recently received very substantial assistance to create an Institute for Computer-Aided Engineering and Management. We are greatly committed to helping the small businessman and entrepreneur realize worthwhile business ideas.

So, at last, it was official. At the time of withdrawing from the project the university had publicly given the reason as being purely financial, despite Professor Makin's own personal reservations about my machine. Now the university had obviously told the minister that their decision had been based, after all, on the likelihood of my device turning out to be a flop, a judgement reached on the results of one set of hurried tests. I felt my old anger return. Why couldn't the university make up its mind as to why exactly they had washed their hands of my machine?

I was also upset at the way the minister had whitewashed the Scottish Development Agency. The Agency, which is entirely funded by central government, may not have been officially approached as he pointed out, but they had been fully aware of my position. At the time of my university project first being made public the Agency, in a Press statement, had pledged its support into looking at ways of assisting in the machine's development. This was in line with their view, privately expressed after a preview they had been given of the television documentary, that the machine should be retained in Scotland, if not in Dundee.

When it later became known that I was to be backed by an Australian company, an Agency spokesman had been quoted in the Press as saying: ' . . . Obviously, the SDA would prefer at the end of the day for the idea to be developed in Scotland. But, nevertheless, the most important thing we feel is that it actually be developed, and if that means it going abroad that will have to be the case.' When I originally read these words I thought my eyes were deceiving me. Here was an organization, dedicated to the creation of jobs within Scotland, allowing future technology to escape to another country without barely batting an eyelid. What had the Agency done to try and keep the project in Scotland? They never said. Certainly they never once approached me.

But what incensed me most of all about the minister's reply was the patronizing tone of the letter; the implication once more that I was going above my station in challenging Newton's laws and therefore

107

it didn't surprise him that British funding was not forthcoming. Whenever I questioned their precious theory the academics scuttled for cover. Now that appeared to be government policy too.

The letter to Education and Science Minister Kenneth Baker was answered by Robert Jackson, his Parliamentary Under-Secretary of State. His letter read:

Thank you for your letter to Kenneth Baker about government support for science and technology. I am replying as this falls within my area of ministerial responsibility. I note your comments about Mr Kidd's invention. However, government support for science has been considerable. We have increased the science budget by more than 14 per cent over general inflation since 1979. At £676 million, it is 9 per cent higher than in 1986–87. Funding for future years is being reviewed in the current public expenditure survey. The problem is that no country can afford to keep pace in all areas with the rapid growth of science and technology. Our policy therefore is to get the very best value from the very substantial funds available by concentrating them on outstanding groups and being more selective about the distribution. You refer to investment in science by other nations. In fact, the government spends more as a percentage of GDP on university and research council research than some of our competitors, notably Japan and the USA. In those countries, however, industry spends more on research than does industry in the UK. OECD figures show that less than 66 per cent of total R & D carried out by industry in 1985 was funded from industry's own resources in the UK, compared with 67 per cent in the USA, 72 per cent in France (in 1984), 76 per cent in Italy, 82 per cent in West Germany, and 98 per cent in Japan (in 1984). In the recent White Paper, 'Civil Research and Development' (Cm 185), the government again emphasized the need for industry to increase the level of R & D that it funds. The Royal Society report on the brain drain provided evidence refuting the proposition that there is a serious loss of scientific talent from Britain. There may be a problem over the quality of UK scientists who emigrate, but our policies on selectivity and concentration should provide a solution. As those policies become increasingly effective, more of our outstanding scientists will have access to first rate facilities.

Whatever Mr Jackson might have said about the government's considerable support for scientific research, such backing certainly did not include space technology. Only the month before, in August 1987, *The Observer*'s science correspondent had written a feature headlined: 'Space – a lost frontier for British science'. In it he commented on the recent resignation of Roy Gibson as director-general of the British National Space Centre following the government's refusal to triple its annual £100 million space budget. He then went on:

> At a time when America and Russia are spending billions, while France and West Germany are each investing about £500 million, and when even India and Italy are paying out moderate sums each year on space science, Britain has decided to cut expenditure to rock bottom. In tax terms, each UK citizen now pays out only the cost of a plate of soup towards space science each year. Such humble expenditure compares with that of Americans who each pay the equivalent of four good dinners in taxes and with the French who stump up with the cost of a three-course lunch for their space budgets.

In the face of such evidence no British government was going to care a tuppeny bun about my project.

Later that year Sir Ian MacGregor, speaking on behalf of the Advanced Energy Research Institute about the establishment of 'Science for Britain', a non-political pressure group, said: 'Britain, while producing some of the greatest inventive geniuses, has often been plagued by a seeming inability to see the creation of its people through to commercial success. Time and again we have witnessed other countries capitalize on British inventions and developments. Frequently, not only the concepts but their innovators have departed this country, impoverishing our unique ability to compete in an ever more scientific and technical international environment to protect and promote our freedom.'

This, of course, was precisely the theme so often taken up by Prince Charles and other notable figures. Everyone, it seemed, deplored what was happening except the government. In my case the Australians had given other interested parties in Britain, including Sir Ian's institute, a 12,000-mile start in reaching my project first, but had still beaten them all to it.

In the midst of all this controversy I also found myself being caught up in a public challenge. Dr James Piggins of Bearsden, Glasgow, threw down the gauntlet in a letter to several newspapers, having just seen the Grampian programme screened in his part of Scotland. He wrote:

> There has been much publicity concerning the device invented by Mr Sandy Kidd, culminating in a half-hour television programme. The inventor claims the machine will open up the secrets of the universe by powering future spacecraft. If I understand the claim correctly, it seems that the device produces lift without a reactive force, thereby defeating Newton's Third Law (that action and reaction are equal and opposite). While Newton's laws require modification at extreme velocities, as Einstein showed, I do not believe Mr Kidd's machine approaches such a regime. I am therefore prepared to offer a prize of £500 to anyone who can prove to the satisfaction of scientists generally (not just Professor Laithwaite) that Mr Kidd's machine does indeed defy Newton's laws. Personally, I believe there is either a reaction which the inventor has overlooked, or else the machine derives its lift, like a helicopter, by displacement of air. Will anybody offer me money to prove it?

I replied to the effect, perhaps rather arrogantly on reflection, that on my way home from collecting the Nobel Prize in Stockholm I would call at the doctor's house, pick up his money, and donate it to a charity of his choice.

What never failed to fascinate me about this whole issue was the way in which my machine generated so much passion in people's attitude towards it. The believers and disbelievers clung to their views as fiercely as people do in politics and religion. It was, therefore, a pleasant change to read someone going into print with a calm, measured approach to scientific advance as seen through the advent of my machine. Norman Barrie, of Dundee, a widely read, retired cinema projectionist, in a letter to the Dundee *Courier*, summed up the situation this way:

> I don't know if Sandy Kidd's gyroscopic propulsion unit works or not, but this I do know, that there are no absolutes in science. It used to be a 'law of nature' that the shortest distance between two points was a straight line, but thanks to

Einstein we know that it's a curve. Lord Kelvin told us that the laws of heat decreed that the sun could not be more than 100 million years old, and therefore Darwin's theory of natural selection was impossible. A few years later came the discovery of radioactivity which showed that the sun was several billion years old and derived its heat from nuclear transmutation. It was 'proved' by Simon Newcomb, an American mathematician, that heavier-than-air flight couldn't take place, almost at the same time that it did take place, by the Wright brothers. So if Sandy Kidd's invention defies Newton's Third Law, but it works and revolutionizes space travel, Newton's absolute will have to go. That is how science in all its branches advances and there is nothing that any individual or any school of thought can do about it.

So the arguments continued to flow backwards and forwards in the public arena. But before August was out that year Janet and I, with the legal contract now finally agreed and the house locked up and the dogs farmed out, had left the war of words behind and were making our way across the world towards Australia.

Chapter 13

Our journey back to Australia, where I was to start the actual building of my new machine, was not the straightforward trip I thought it was going to be. Several days before leaving Scotland, BWN asked me to bring one of my earlier machines with me and go first to a destination in the United States. They wanted me to head for the town of Boulder in Colorado for a meeting with an engineer called Mark Beran. He acted as their consultant in North America and had agreed to evaluate my work.

I decided to take my original prototype which, although heavier and more cumbersome than any of its successors, was by then well-tried and could be relied upon consistently to produce lift. I simply wrapped the whole thing up in a towel and put it into one of the cases, hoping that no customs officer would spot it and ask me to explain what it was.

Boulder turned out to be one of the most delightful, beautifully-kept towns I had ever been to. It is about thirty miles from the state capital of Denver and sits on the edge of the Great Plains with the overpowering presence of the Rocky Mountains just to the west. Boulder is home to the University of Colorado whose campus gives the whole town a soothing, laid-back atmosphere devoid of the hassle one normally associates with American towns of this size. It has also built up a prosperous spread of high technology industry, creating a pool of skilled manpower and specialist services. It can provide anything an engineer is ever likely to need which is one reason why Mark Beran stayed on as an engineering consultant after a spell with the local division of IBM in research and development. His home and adjoining workshop were just a few miles out from Boulder in a small, residential community called Niwot, an old Indian word meaning left-handed. The name had seemingly been chosen for no other reason than because this had at one time been the stamping ground of a chief of the Arapaho tribe who had done everything with his left hand.

Beran had taken a master's degree in mechanical engineering at the University of Florida and then gone off to Germany with a Fulbright scholarship for post-graduate studies at a technical university in Munich. He had, of course, been told I would be dropping in to see him with a machine which did the unexpected, but it wasn't until I turned up at the old Indian Reserve with my case, which incidentally had gone unchallenged by customs, that he realized I had brought him a real box of tricks.

My first task was to get the machine fully rigged and running so that Mark could judge everything for himself and then possibly get to work on some physics which would be helpful to me later on in Australia. Having brought only the bare machine and the small engine for the gyros, I now had to adapt the device to another precession drive for rotating the entire unit. There had obviously been no way I was going to hump my heavy electrical drill across the Atlantic. Mark had a drive of his own. It was now simply a case of rebuilding the top end of the machine to fit in with its design. This meant different bushes, bearings, pulleys, pins and gear wheels. Normally this could have posed a problem at short notice. But not in Boulder. Here they have McGuckins, reputed to be the finest hardware store on the planet. There you can get anything from the humblest washer to the most sophisticated machine component. The premises resemble a vast supermarket with its aisles laid out on a grid pattern, lettered and numbered in such a way that you can easily find the exact location of the item you want. There is a saying in local engineering circles which goes like this: 'The time required to prototype a new design is directly proportional to the distance from the lab to McGuckin's Hardware.'

With a facility like this on hand, therefore, I had everything running and lifting without a hitch in less than a week of arriving. Mark, like all the others before him, was intrigued but greatly puzzled. Then I was told to stand by to give a repeat performance for Noel and Bob Carroll who were going to fly in from Los Angeles to see the machine for themselves. A few days later they duly arrived. In many ways this was to be one of the most crucial demonstrations so far. I felt it was really imperative that Noel, in particular, was given a good impression of the machine's capability at the outset of my work for BWN in view of the way he had embarked upon the project on the basis of what had, in actuality, been second-hand evidence. He had never seen the machine run in my garage. He had only been able to stroke it. I could think of nothing more demoralizing than arriving

113

in Australia to build another machine with the first one having just failed to produce the goods for the man who was footing the bill for its future development.

The two brothers arrived at Boulder in the evening with little time to spare before moving on to their next destination. If I remember correctly Noel was on his way to Saudi Arabia, giving one of his impressive impersonations of a perpetual motion machine. The device had to be shown right away and it was almost midnight when they gathered in Mark's workshop. The atmosphere was taut. No one said a word as I went through the start-up procedures. I sensed I was on trial although no one had put it in exactly these terms. The machine roared into life, followed by the gyros which I then started driving up through the rev range. I waited, anxious as ever, until the speeds of both the device and the gyros reached mating point to create the vertical thrust. I heard a gasp of delight from the onlookers as the machine lifted off the bench against the counterweight. I let it hover for a full minute before dropping it back to earth. Each run was the same. A consistent lift of half a pound. Everyone, including myself, was delighted. I felt as though I had passed some sort of entrance examination. It was now one o'clock in the morning, breakfast time in Scotland. I decided to put in an alarm call to the family and tell them the good news. After ten days in Boulder I was now well and truly on my way to Australia.

* * * * *

Our new home in Australia was a three-bedroomed spacious chalet in a private residential area only a few miles out from Dandenong. The estate was located on high ground called Endeavour Hills, a rather appropriate place I thought for someone like myself to end up in. The house and its setting were not all that different from our own home in Dundee. It was only when you went into the garden with its different flowers, birds, and creepy-crawlies that you fully realized how nature had provided another sort of infrastructure for a climate much hotter than our own. Indeed, in the ensuing months Janet and I were nearly fried alive during a heatwave summer which saw temperatures soar into the high thirties Celsius. Unfortunately our house had no air conditioning and by evening we almost suffocated from the heat indoors. Some nights it was so intolerable I was forced to hose down the roof.

From a shopping point of view Janet found herself in a kind

114

of paradise. Meat, fruit and vegetables of excellent quality were all much cheaper than back home. Cigarettes, alcohol and petrol also cost a lot less. Our weekly shopping bill came to about £20 instead of the normal £50. Some things were, of course, more expensive but overall we felt the average wage in Australia provided a better standard of living than in Britain. We, therefore, weren't suffering any material hardship and, with a car at our disposal, we had the means of exploring the glorious beaches and the vast up-country expanses of Victoria.

At work also I had no difficulty in settling down. The atmosphere in the BWN plant was relaxed and friendly. My arrival from Scotland with a mystery machine on a hush-hush project obviously created a great deal of curiosity. When people in the factory asked me questions about my work I had to be discreet. But my 'cover' was blown after only a few weeks. The *Sundaay Express* carried a big feature about me at the end of September and the cutting duly appeared on the factory notice board. For security purposes, however, I had been given a small place of my own to work in, with back-up from the shop floor for anything I required. The drawings for my new machine were now complete and although I could have made everything myself, it was decided to contract out the work for the sake of speeding things on. By the end of October I had the machine almost assembled. It was made from high duty aluminium to keep the weight down to three pounds. It was ten inches tall, six inches in diameter, and had five-inch gyros. The power to drive both the machine and the gyros by belts and pulleys came from two variable-speed electric motors of half and one-quarter horse power operated by variable-speed controllers.

The principle of the machine remained the same. However, instead of using eccentrics to pull the gyros in towards the central shaft during precession, I decided to employ a camshaft fitted to the top of the device. The cam would perform exactly the same function although it would make the machine noisier and reduce the smoothness of its action. But it was much easier to make than the more sophisticated eccentrics and, as I expected this to be a transitional device, the cam would be ideal for the purpose. In general, this device was of an improved engineering design. For example, all the plain bearings had been replaced by ballraces or, as they are more commonly known, ball bearings. These would reduce frictional drag, thereby enhancing the machine's ability to produce lift. I wanted the same pulsing action, but more powerful, than I

115

had achieved with my previous machine fitted with eccentrics.

That is exactly what I got in my first trial runs at the beginning of November. The machine was being kicked up off the bench by the pulsative forces being released by the gyros each time they flew back out. It was a strong, consistent effect which could be held and controlled whenever I got the gyros within a certain speed band. I was overjoyed at having proved once again that the original device was no freak. I had now given the Australians a machine of their own well within the six-month proving phase. Noel Carroll was also delighted when he saw it perform, although he did not quite share my exuberance in believing that I had proved beyond doubt it was possible to produce a reactionless force contrary to the laws of physics. Noel thought it was still too early to make such claims and raise hopes prematurely. He felt there could still be several other explanations for the way the machine was behaving and these would have to be eliminated through further investigation before we started to speak about a breakthrough. As far as he was concerned the proving phase was still not over. Nevertheless, I was well pleased with what I had achieved since leaving Scotland ten weeks earlier. My original machine had proved itself yet again at its critical debut in Colorado. Now my latest device had come up trumps in Australia. It was an opportune time for a breather. Janet and I were anxious to get home to see the family and check over the house. Noel agreed that we should return to Scotland for the festive season and not come back until early January. After talks with BWN's patent attorneys, preparing the ground for another patent application to cover the new machine, we headed for the airport, arriving home on November 7.

There was, of course, another lengthy debriefing session with all our folks, answering their countless questions on our life style down under. The feeling still persisted, encouraged by newspaper speculation, that I was in line for a huge pot of gold. What most people simply didn't understand was the long-term nature of a project like this. The proving phase was only the start. After that would come an unlimited period of development to improve the machine to the point of commercial application and beyond. This would involve problems of stress, stability and design. At times I could see no end to the work that lay ahead. Wealth and fame were still a long way off, if at all.

In the meantime, however, my confidence in the future was greatly boosted by wholehearted support from a totally unexpected quarter. Dr Harold Aspden, a highly qualified scientist and engineer, wrote me a letter explaining how he had been following the fortunes of my machine. For nearly twenty years he had been in charge of the European patent operations of IBM before retiring early to become a visiting Senior Research Fellow at Southampton University. His Cambridge Ph.D. was for research on electromagnetism. His particular interest lay in the growing belief that tremendous amounts of energetic activity existed in the vacuum of space and one day this could be made to interact with man-made machines, both to improve our energy resources and develop space travel.

> . . . Your machine is really telling us that the law of action and reaction is not sacrosanct, even in a practical and demonstrable machine. This is something that Professor Laithwaite has also been saying concerning gyroscopes and what I have been saying in connection with electrodynamics. Both of us think that it means there is a real ether that can be pushed against. This is something that disturbs those who believe in Einstein's theory, but the implications are really far-reaching. . . . The case I put is that a breach of Newton's laws proves that there is a hidden medium filling space which can interact with matter to cause anomalous forces or states of spin. This can lead us to a solution of the mysteries of the solar system, eg why the sun and all the planets could be created with spin in the same direction, and allow us to accept a law of electrodynamic force that gives the unifying link with gravitation. Einstein sought this unification in terms of his theory but without success. It needs something like your machine to force the scientific community to be more critical of Einstein's methods and look with more favour on the revival of the ether. I hope you will see from this that your machine means far more than promise of new methods of transportation. It could cause a revolution in physics by reviving interest in the ether and thereby making it respectable to search for methods of tapping the vast amounts of energy that are stored in that elusive but all-enveloping medium from which the stars, our sun and, of course, our earth were created.

Dr Aspden had done nothing to disguise his motives in supporting my work. It gave him valuable, high-profile evidence in gaining further credence for his own commitment to the principle of unseen energy. Professor Laithwaite had similarly stood to profit through my machine, recognizing it as an endorsement of his own views on anti-gravity propulsion. They were both on my side so who was I to argue? There was no way I was going to look such gift-horses in the mouth. In any case, who at this stage was to say that Laithwaite, Aspden and Ferrier were wrong and the Dundee University team of Makin, Davidson and Thomson were right? The gulf that separated these two schools of thought was as deep as space itself.

★ ★ ★ ★ ★

When I reported back to Dandenong in the middle of January, 1988, after the Christmas and New Year break, I was under the impression that my first task was to improve the performance of my latest machine. Much to my astonishment, however, I was told that the next step was going to be scientific evaluation. My machine was going to be put through strict laboratory trials by a team of independent engineers. The results would show whether the device was, in fact, producing a genuine lifting force and, if so, exactly how much. In other words, was my machine really able to shed weight in overcoming the downward pull of gravity?

I realized that positive results gained under clinical conditions would eliminate secondary effects such as vibration, friction and aerodynamics and would, therefore, help to subdue a good many of my critics. You may think I should have welcomed such an opportunity. But I didn't see it that way at the time. I was extremely upset at having to stand trial in this fashion because of the deeply ingrained dogma of the Establishment. As far as I was concerned I had already proved my case. I wasn't really interested in trying to convert the textbook Johnnies or rewrite the laws of physics. Come to that, winning the Nobel Prize wasn't my main consideration either. I knew that if the laboratory tests proved my machine was genuine, and I had absolutely no doubt that they would, the critics would still not accept the results as conclusive. They would simply want more machines and more evidence. It would be a never-ending process of trying to convert the unconvertible. As an engineer I would have preferred to spend all this time and effort developing my machine into viable commercial products, things that could be seen to work despite what theory said to the contrary. As far as I was concerned the proving phase was over. But Noel Carroll believed otherwise. He was paying the piper so I had to play the tune.

Back in Britain, however, other business interests were only just waking up to the existence of my machine and wanting to get in on the action. Their appearance on the scene arose through the screening of the Grampian documentary programme by Central Television, the Birmingham-based station covering the thickly populated industrial Midlands with a potential audience of ten million. The programme had not been networked simultaneously throughout the country, but bought on a piecemeal basis by certain other commercial companies who then slotted it into their own schedules. Scottish Television had shown it to the rest of Scotland in June, the month after Grampian had originally transmitted it in the north-east of Scotland. HTV followed in Wales, also in June, and Tyne Tees put it out in the north-east of England in August. The programme had also been selected for screening at the Edinburgh Television Festival that summer. But the big breakthrough came with Central's decision to show 'The Man Who Wants to Change the World' at the prime time of half-past ten at night on Thursday, January 7, 1988. This, by the way, compared to Scottish Television's attempt to 'bury' the programme, all about a Scots inventor, at one-thirty on a Saturday afternoon. Speak about a prophet having no voice in his own land!

The reaction to this latest transmission was swift. Two companies, a house building contractor in Nottingham and a foundry group near Derby, came forward with offers to discuss funding. Both firms were headed by self-made millionaires who had struggled for success and could identify with my particular battle against the odds. They had both seen the programme and been inspired by the story. But they were unaware that the programme had been first shown eight months previously and was now somewhat out of date. When they discovered that an Australian company had already moved in they were disappointed but asked to be remembered if circumstances were to change. I wonder what would have happened if Central Television had shown the programme much earlier? It is possible that I might never have ended up in a small Australian town called Dandenong.

BWN themselves were aware of this fresh interest being stimulated in my project back home. Leonard Holihan, the chief executive of the Advanced Energy Research Institute, who had originally made contact with me the previous summer, had written to Noel Carroll offering his co-operation in developing the 'tremendous potential of gyroscopic propulsion'. He explained that the institute, being

119

a catalyst body matching innovation to expertise and funding, had established an 'invisible college' of scientists, boffins and industrialists. Professor Laithwaite and Dr Aspden were two of their key advisors. He now wished to place all this back-up at BWN's disposal. But Noel already had his own plans for the machine. At this stage he wanted to play it his way.

Only on the subject of publicity did I feel justified in asserting myself. Even though the firm's name was not being revealed, Noel wanted as little said as possible about the project until he had gathered enough evidence to present a cast-iron case for the machine. He was very anxious to avoid having egg on his face if things didn't work out according to plan. I, of course, took a different view. It was publicity that had put me where I was. Without it I would still have been soldiering on in my garden shed like so many other inventors whose efforts had never been given the exposure they required to stimulate public interest. When Noel signed me up, he realized he was also inheriting a publicity machine which had created a momentum of public interest that simply couldn't be halted in mid-stream. So, he put a brave face on it, even when I told him that Ron Thompson was coming out to Melbourne to research a feature for *The Observer*'s colour magazine. By now, of course, I was well-accustomed to the ways of the media but this particular assignment really opened my eyes and nearly drove me mad into the bargain.

Thompson had been told that the pictures to go with his article would be taken by Carolyn Johns, a partner in a Sydney photographic agency. She duly arrived in Dandenong one evening and I assumed she would take a couple of quick snaps and get on her way as all the other photographers had done. But no. First of all she wanted to recce the location she had chosen for the main picture. It was at Point Ormond on Port Phillip Bay, a few miles down the coast from Melbourne. On a prominent hillock, right at the water's edge, there stood a twenty-five-foot-high, wooden-slatted construction which at one time had acted as a navigational aid for shipping. She wanted me sitting on the slope of the hillock, holding my machine, with the tall frame behind me looking almost like a launching pad of some sort. The photograph had to be taken at night under a clear, starry sky. She was anxious to compose a portrait which would have a subtle, futuristic atmosphere about it.

Ron volunteered to act as my stand-in during rehearsals so it was he who crawled out of bed at the back of three the following morning

120

to accompany Carolyn to Point Ormond. When they arrived at the hillock she asked him to adopt a number of poses while she took a series of photographs with her instant camera. For the next hour he took up different positions on the grass while Carolyn circled round him clicking away furiously.

Ron could only shake his head in bewilderment when he told us about it all later over breakfast. 'It was one of the most bizarre situations I've ever been involved in,' he said ruefully. 'There was I hopping around in semi-darkness being followed by a woman with a camera. It must have all looked a bit kinky. In fact, I could see a number of prostitutes hovering in the vicinity thinking I was a likely client. Then a police car drew up for several minutes to view the proceedings. Finally a passer-by tried to get off with Carolyn. I began to think the whole thing was a dream.'

Janet and I kept choking over our cereal, unable to contain ourselves, while Ron unfolded the tale in mock horror. But our turn was still to come. Later that day Carolyn went off to Tasmania for an assignment with Olivia Newton-John, saying she would be back in a week's time to take the real thing. By then Ron had left for home. When we reported to the hillock with my machine as arranged at nine o'clock at night, Carolyn was already there with an assistant getting everything ready on the 'set'. There was a smoke machine, coloured flashes, lights and goodness knows what else. I even had to put on a special raincoat which was all the fashion in Australia at that time. It was modelled on what the stockmen wore and was supposed to improve your macho image.

I thought the session was never going to end. The trouble was that the weather wasn't quite right for the photograph she was after. There was a bit of a breeze which kept wafting the smoke away and cloud was blanking out the stars. Nevertheless Carolyn stuck doggedly to her task and fairly put me through the mill. I kept thinking that if this was what professional models had to put up with then I was jolly glad I had chosen the relatively simple task of trying to open up the universe.

Because of the lack of moonlight, Carolyn finally explained she would need to take the photograph on a two-minute exposure. Could I sit motionless, and not even breathe, for that length of time? I said I was willing to try anything to get home to bed. When at last she had got what she wanted it was after midnight and I was nearly at screaming point. I swore I would never have another photograph taken. But I soon relented when I saw the result of Carolyn's work.

Her colour picture was superb, well worth all the effort that had gone into it.

The article itself led to a follow-up interview on the John Dunn Show on BBC national radio. Inevitably, all this fresh publicity generated another considerable batch of mail, mostly from enthusiastic amateurs anxious to know more about the machine. But one letter brought a generous offer of technical help from one of Britain's top engineers. He was Rupert Lucas who had just retired from Rolls Royce as chief development engineer of the company's Helicopter Engine Group. Like myself he had been so inspired by Professor Laithwaite's Christmas television lecture on gyroscopes in 1974 that he, too, had gone on to conduct experiments of his own. He wrote:

> I was delighted to hear you have taken up the topic and would like to offer my help. I believe that my background is very relevant and that I could help you in two ways: firstly to get your demonstrator to work at convincing levels of effect and secondly to provide some academic respectability in interpreting and presenting the results. There are plenty of disbelievers about when one of the fundamental principles is questioned.

He believed that to produce indisputable results the machine and the gyros would have to be run at high speeds, with the design of the gyros being altered to withstand the additional stresses involved.

But the sceptics were still thick on the ground. From Oxford, a technical writer and author wrote to Ron Thompson telling him that his article in *The Observer* had depressed him. 'This thing has clearly got completely out of hand,' he said. 'Mr Kidd is no longer amusing himself in his garage. He is now spending large sums of other people's money . . . When Mr Kidd finally discovers what it is he has "invented" the disappointment will shatter him . . . I think at the very least I ought to write to Mr Carroll explaining how the machine functions so that he can pull his own chestnuts out of the fire.' He was convinced my machine was lifting purely through aerodynamic effect. He cited the example of the golf ball, whereby the dimples on the ball reduce drag and allow it to travel a greater distance. He said that if I were to apply the same principle to my gyros by milling their edges I would get an even greater vertical lift.

I was not amused one little bit by the patronizing tone of this letter. But when the writer was informed that the machine had continued to produce thrust even when the gyros had been covered, a fact which had ruled out aerodynamic effect in the mind of Bill Ferrier and others, he still refused to be convinced. He replied in a second letter: 'I have always been willing to accept that other forces may be involved. My point was that aerodynamic lift was the first and most likely source of lift and any experimenter who did not take the basic precaution of running the machine in a vacuum was wasting his time as well as insulting our intelligence . . . I am not convinced that housings will necessarily make the machine aerodynamically neutral. Aerodynamics is an extremely complex subject and the pattern of pressures around a gyro, even when housed, is almost impossible to imagine. If it is not practicable to test in a vacuum chamber, at least take a series of measurements inside a diver's decompression chamber at different pressures. That would give some indication of the role aerodynamics plays.'

He then went on to make further dismissive remarks about my original device. He first described it as a 'whirly-gig'. A few pages later he said: 'People seem so hypnotized by the whirling wheels and Heath-Robinson linkages of the machine that they've lost sight of the simple, underlying mechanism.' He concluded by suggesting that the Kidd machine was similar to the Chernobyl nuclear disaster in Russia in the sense that it was 'a tale of human over-confidence, error and gullibility, coupled with important technical considerations.'

By now, of course, I was quite hardened to such scathing criticism. From the very start I had known this would be par for the course. Professor Laithwaite had also warned me about the 'slings and arrows of outrageous fortune'. But happily I had the temperament to cope with all the verbal missiles. This type of reaction simply stiffened my determination to win acceptance for my work in the end. In any case, I had more important considerations on my mind. I had to prepare my latest machine for its critical laboratory test. I was praying that the results would put the doubting Thomases to rest.

Chapter 14

The company chosen by BWN to conduct the tests was called VIPAC, one of the leading engineering and research consultancy groups in south-east Asia, based at the Victorian Technology Centre in Port Melbourne. The firm employed over forty professional engineers and could undertake a wide range of specialist services ranging from acoustics and vibration analysis to engineering dynamics and fatigue studies. They had worked on advanced acoustic systems for the Royal Australian Navy and had designed the acoustic and noise control system for Singapore's famous Changi Airport. John Simmons was then their principal vibration engineer when he came to the BWN plant in January, 1988, to discuss the forthcoming laboratory project.

He and his colleagues had already devised a test procedure for the machine which would subject it to the toughest set of conditions possible. If my device had somehow been deceiving us all into believing it had anti-gravity properties then these tests would expose it for what it was worth. Every eventuality would be covered. There would be no margin for error. This test would leave no stone unturned.

Simmons explained that the machine would be put into a sealed container and suspended in mid-air at the end of a cord attached to an overhead beam fitted with strain gauges. When the machine was run in this position it would be unable to react on air or solid surface. But if, despite that, it was still able to 'climb' by losing weight then such a force would be detected by the strain gauges and the information fed into electronic analysing equipment where it would be statistically processed and measured. There would also be a pen-trace print-out of precisely how the machine was behaving. Because of the way the gyros moved in and out during precession, releasing their forces in rapid succession, the machine would be registering an upward movement and a downward movement. If the device was genuine then it would go up more than it would come

124

down and the difference between the two would be the measure of its anti-gravity thrust. According to Newton's Third Law, however, the up forces would always be balanced out by the down forces and there would be no change in weight. The result of the test would be zero, just as it would be if a person were to go into such a box and jump up and down attempting by some magical means to become lighter in the process.

What I had to do, therefore, was to build a container large enough to accommodate the machine in the top compartment, with the engine and all its gearing, along with the fuel and water tanks, in the bottom section. It would have been permissible to have kept the fuel and water supplies separate from the container and fed them into the machine by pipelines. I was determined, however, to have everything self-contained and 'quarantined' from contact with external influences. This, I knew, was being ultra cautious but I simply didn't want anyone to suggest later that the twisting action of the machine was gaining leverage on supply lines to assist it in producing vertical thrust.

By insisting on having a closed system like this I realized I would be adding to the overall weight of the container. Although this would have absolutely no bearing on the way the machine was able to create its lift, it would have a significant effect on the final calculation of thrust which would be given as a percentage of the total weight of the entire unit. There was no way, therefore, that I was prepared to carry the two variable-speed electric motors which I had been using to drive the gyros and the device on the test bench. With their weight of forty pounds on top of everything else, any percentage lift would be reduced to a ridiculous fraction. I decided to revert to an internal combustion engine, but one that would have to be adapted to drive both the gyros and the machine, the first time I had attempted to do this with a single power unit. Such an engine would have to accommodate the speeds of both. It was absolutely vital that these were properly matched up and synchronized. To achieve this I had to build a completely new gear box with special gears cut for this particular task.

Here, again, I was faced with a choice: metal gears or non-metal ones made from a synthetic material like Delrin. Metal gears could be made much more quickly and would be the strongest available. But the metal-to-metal contact would cause 'glitching', which would severely interfere with the signal to the radio control throttle. I had encountered this when flying model aeroplanes. Non-metal gears would not create this problem and could, therefore, be controlled quite simply by a remote system. But these gears could not be easily acquired and would not have the strength of metal. In the end I opted for metal gears. It would mean, of course, that during the tests the engine would have to be set manually each time at what I would have to guess was the right speed and then left to run on its own. However, this seemed to be a reasonable set up at the time.

In choosing the material for the container I went for plywood. It was light yet strong. I cut a hole in the side of the box for the engine's exhaust pipe to avoid taking it out the top or the bottom where the emission could have created an upward or a downward thrust against the air. When completed the box was sixteen inches in height and nine inches square. With the machine and all its services the total weight of the unit was twelve pounds.

Throughout this period of preparation I felt rather isolated at BMW, having little contact with senior members of the company and not receiving anything in the way of encouragement or moral support. I was aware that certain people frowned on my machine and were convinced that the laboratory results would go against me. At times I felt terribly lonely, even with Janet at my side waiting for me to return each evening to our temporary home at Endeavour Hills. But I simply had to keep going. Although I still had absolute faith in my machine, I knew that the laboratory trials would present a stiff challenge to us both. Neither the man nor the machine had operated under such conditions before.

The Victorian Technology Centre is a double-storey building situated in one of the more attractive parts of Port Melbourne not, as I thought it might be, down at the docks among the warehouses and factories of this important shipping and trading city. The sightseeing aspect of the area, however, was the consideration furthest from my mind as I drove slowly through a maze of unfamiliar streets to reach the VIPAC laboratories and deliver my boxed machine as requested, two days before the tests were due to begin on March 1. The engineers there required my machine in advance to calibrate their equipment and no doubt to check it over to make certain it complied with the description I had previously given them. I almost felt like someone who had just taken a close friend to hospital for a major operation as I drove back to Endeavour Hills that hot and stuffy evening. But I knew the machine was in safe and capable hands. Those people who would have access to it were all covered by a non-disclosure agreement issued by BWN and, in any case, the very nature of their work carried a built-in guarantee of confidentiality.

On the big day Janet came with me to the laboratories. She had been my constant companion throughout all the difficult years I had been involved in my anti-gravity project. She had been a tremendous support, not perhaps understanding all the technicalities of the various machines but always being there to share in the agonies and ecstasies of it all. It now seemed quite natural that she should be present at the great moment of truth. I had no idea, of course, how long these tests would take. Perhaps only a few hours. It very much depended on how the machine behaved in its new set-up. I simply assumed that as soon as we succeeded in getting two or three positive runs we would be finished and on our way. Apart from any other consideration, a laboratory project like this tied up expensive manpower and equipment and did not come cheaply.

When we arrived at the centre just after nine in the morning we were met by John Simmons himself. He was a neatly built man of medium height with black bushy hair and beard. He was to take charge of the tests personally, assisted by Richard Fraser, another highly qualified engineer. Two other members of staff were also standing by to help. The machine had already been set up for the test. The laboratory was dominated by a gantry ten feet high with the uprights eight feet apart. The box was hanging from the crossarm on a Kevlar cord which allowed it to dangle about three feet from the floor. Wires from each corner of the top of the box had been drawn together and attached to the end of the cord so that the unit was hanging absolutely plumb. The top section of the box containing the machine was completely closed in and sealed. The bottom section with the engine and all its backup was open and accessible. Loose cords had been attached to each side of the box and anchored to the pillars of the gantry. This was to prevent the unit being swung about under torque reaction during the acceleration period.

As I gazed round the room and saw the line-up of equipment which had been assembled for the test – the signal analysers, strain amplifier, digital plotter, data recorder, accelerometer and all the other electronic technology – I couldn't help comparing this engineering clinic with the crude conditions of my garage back in Scotland. It was all slightly intimidating. But John Simmons and Richard Fraser went out of their way to put me at ease in this strange environment. Their natural friendliness created an informal and relaxed atmosphere. I never for an instant got the feeling that they regarded my machine as a gimmick and these tests as a waste of time with a foregone conclusion. Like all the best referees they were strictly impartial. By the same token they also made it perfectly clear that the rules of the game would be strictly adhered to. They explained carefully what the procedure would be.

Each test run would have a duration of at least thirty seconds and be conducted in exactly the same way. Having manually set the machine to run at what I thought was the correct speed, I would then not be allowed to touch the box again until the run had ended. If I did, that result would be instantly invalidated. If during the series I altered the character of the machine in any way we would have to go back to the beginning and start the tests all over again. Immediately before and after each run a background reading would be taken of the ambient vibration level in the laboratory. If the machine's output was not of a percentage significantly greater than the highest of these readings, that test run would be nullified. There is, of course, a certain degree of vibration present all the time in the environment which is due to a multitude of factors, anything from an earth tremor to road traffic. This creates 'noise' which may not be noticeable to the human senses but could have a critical bearing on a situation as sensitive as the tests we were carrying out.

I would be able to monitor the behaviour of the machine during each run by watching the build up of the pulses on a small visual display unit. Within ten seconds of the run starting I would know if the device was producing lift. When it finished I would be told how good a run it had been. I would then have to wait about twenty minutes to get the exact measurement before starting the next run. This was the way I wanted it to be. I did not want to proceed blindly from one run to another without knowing the amount of lift I was getting. This information would help me in setting the speed each time.

Everything was set to go. I glanced at my watch. It was ten o'clock. They would all be in bed and asleep back home. Janet gave me a smile of encouragement as I stepped up to my machine, almost like a boxer coming out of his corner, and started the engine. I throttled it up until I judged it was running at the correct speed then stepped smartly back. I looked anxiously at the monitor and then at John. Nothing was happening. The pulses were going flat across the screen. Mechanically the machine was running well enough. I could hear it whirring round inside the sealed compartment of the box. But the instrumentation was registering a zero effect. There was nothing going up or coming down. I tried two more runs, but again the results were the same. Blank. This meant only one thing. I had not properly matched the speeds of the gyros and the machine in the gearing of the engine. There was, of course, no way I could rectify that in a hurry. It would have meant a new gear box. I would now simply have to alter the machine itself to make it compatible with the speeds available.

I cursed under my breath. This was the last thing I had wanted to happen. But I had always known that such a problem might arise. Synchronizing the speeds was a tricky business requiring an element of luck. I had, however, come prepared for such a contingency. I quickly attached weights to the gyros. Making them heavier would increase the centrifugal force which, in turn, would hold down the wheels and force them to work harder. I signalled to John and Richard that I was ready to go again.

This time we got results. But, unbelievably, they were negative. In other words the machine was generating a downward force only. It was, in effect, getting heavier instead of lighter and, therefore, doing the very opposite of what it was supposed to be doing. I was taken completely by surprise. No one had ever mentioned the possibility of the machine going into reverse in this way. In fact my reaction was to question the test equipment. I asked John if it had been connected up the right way. He smiled and asked me if my machine was the right way up inside the box. I took his point. Professionals simply didn't make fundamental errors of that sort. 'This result is very significant in itself,' John assured me, examining the pen-trace print-out. 'It is just as impossible to achieve as the actual claim you are making for the machine!'

I was less interested, however, in the academic implications of what the machine had just accomplished than I was in getting it to work the way it should. Conscious that I was under the scrutiny of others, I feverishly got to work on the machine, this time putting on a completely new set of gyros. When we got going again the first results started coming up positive. My hopes began to soar. Then almost immediately the machine began to malfunction. I quickly discovered the belt drive was slipping and I would need to return to the factory to carry out repairs. Things were not going smoothly but I felt sure I was now on the right track.

I worked through most of that night testing and retesting the machine for reliability. Finally, at four o'clock, I was satisfied with the way it was running and fell into bed for a couple of hours' sleep. The next morning Janet and I drove back through the teeming breakfast-time traffic of Melbourne to reach the technology centre with the repaired machine. By mid-morning it was rigged once more and ready for action. Because I had altered the parameters of the device by changing gyros the testing had to start again from square one. As I got ready to fire up the engine I knew that if I didn't get results now I was in trouble. The trials would have to be delayed indefinitely while I carried out more detailed adjustments back at the workshop in Dandenong. John and Richard were standing by in their white coats looking like hospital consultants hovering over a patient. Then we started. The background reading was taken first and then I was told to go.

I throttled up the engine and stepped back well clear of the box. Fifteen seconds later I was the happiest man in Australia. The machine was showing definite lift. It was losing weight! 'Positive run, Sandy,' said John quietly as we watched the pattern of pulses build up on the small television screen. After a minute the run was ended and the calculations began. Twenty minutes later I was told the lift factor had been two ounces. I could have jumped over the moon. I knew then I had made it. Barring further mechanical failures there was no reason why the machine shouldn't now carry on producing its anti-gravity force. Several more runs yielded the same positive results. The machine was definitely defying physics. This was a clinical judgement carried out by the most advanced equipment available and not one simply based on a crude counterweight system.

When BWN phoned in to the laboratory for a progress report they were told the device was running positively. Within half an hour Noel Carroll and two others from the factory were on the scene being briefed by John Simmons on what had been happening. I now assumed the tests would be over. But Noel had other ideas. He now wanted us to carry on and complete a series of twenty statistical runs. I told him we already had the evidence he wanted. Furthermore, the machine with its manual engine control didn't really lend itself to that number of runs. I would have to set the engine by ear each time. Had I known about this at the outset I would certainly have adapted my machine to a radio control system. But Noel was adamant. It had to be done.

We started at noon and finished at lunchtime the following day. Each run was a positive success. There had not been a single zero result. The lift had varied from just below half an ounce to four ounces. Each force measurement had been well in excess of the highest background reading. At several stages I volunteered to carry out slight adjustments which I was certain would have increased the lift. But each time I was told to keep going with the machine exactly as it was. As long as the results were positive that was all that counted at this stage. John Simmons was adamant on this point. Nevertheless, there were times during those days when I would have given anything for a radio control throttle. If only I could have adjusted speeds during the actual runs there was no doubt in my mind that the force would have been increased.

News of what was happening in the laboratory spread quickly round the building until people from other departments started coming in to see things for themselves. There was, of course, nothing to see except a box dangling at the end of a cord. The container wasn't even moving under the torquing action of the machine. The loose cords had never been needed. This was another plus factor as far as the results were concerned because it meant the machine could not have been using taut wires as leverage to assist in producing vertical thrust.

As we had progressed through the series of tests John and Richard had obviously been gripped by quiet excitement. Neither of them had ever seen anything like this before. Privately they may never have believed it possible. Now they were faced with the evidence of their own test procedure, one they had devised to satisfy the high standards of verification demanded within their own profession. One of the high-ups in VIPAC also came into the laboratory. I heard him ask if the news he had heard was correct. 'Absolutely true,' replied John. 'But don't ask me how the machine is doing it. I simply don't have the answers.'

Suddenly, it seemed, I was being congratulated by all and sundry. Noel Carroll was as happy as a cat with a bowl of cream. He purred away with pleasure, delighted that the hunch he had decided to play nine months previously in Dundee had paid off. After two and a half days in the laboratory I felt emotionally drained. I simply wanted to escape for a spell and sort out my thoughts. What would the critics say now, I wondered? If they didn't accept the results then they would have to explain why not. They would find it difficult to challenge the integrity of the tests themselves. VIPAC had been meticulous to a fault in the way they had carried them out. Nothing had been done to favour the machine. In fact, the odds had been stacked against it. The lift had certainly not been as high as it could have been and it didn't match the measurements I had calculated on my original machine. But the ounces of lift obtained were, as Professor Laithwaite might have said, pure and wholesome and free from the contamination of error. Whatever excuses some people might give for not accepting the results as conclusive, and no doubt there would be plenty in that category, no one could take these results away from me. They would never go away. They would, however insignificantly, take their place in scientific history.

It took VIPAC a little time to carry out a detailed analysis and extrapolation of the raw results and bring out their findings in a formal report. When they did the lift factor was expressed in two different ways. It was first given as a percentage of the peak upward forces generated, that is the degree to which the machine was going up more than it was going down. The average over the twenty runs was 2.2 per cent of the peak force, equal to 1.8 ounces. This was absolute force standing on its own irrespective of the mass of the machine. It was also after subtraction of the effect of any background ambient vibration.

But when that 2.2 per cent was calculated as a fraction of the total weight of the boxed machine, it was reduced to 1 per cent. In other words the profit margin had been severely eroded by the overheads it had been forced to carry: the box, fuel and water tanks, the engine and gears. I have always contended that the fairest way to work out this figure is to use the net weight of the machine only, free from all these extras. If that had been the case the relative weight would have been only two and a half pounds instead of twelve and that 1 per cent would have gone up to nearly 5 per cent.

But there was another critical aspect of these results which the report went on to examine in great detail. This was called the confidence level. It was all very well getting twenty positive results out of twenty consecutive runs but was this a fluke? If a thousand tests had been carried out would the result have been a thousand out of a thousand or would the average, instead of being 2.2 per cent, have worked out as zero? Had these twenty tests been a typical sample or had they simply been a lucky cluster? The report posed these questions. To find the answers John Simmons and his team broke the results down into various components to examine their values and pattern of distribution. Then, by using statistical analysis, they built up a final picture against which these twenty results could be fully evaluated.

They concluded that there was only a 3.3 per cent probability that the results had been drawn from a hypothetical population of results where the final average would have worked out as zero. In other words they were 96.7 per cent confident that our non-zero result was correct. That figure was based on the assumption that there had been a normal distribution of the various elements of the generated force over the sample twenty runs. Because the results showed only an 80 per cent certainty that this had been the case, the final confidence level was reduced to 77 per cent. This was how certain they were, taking all the 'ifs' and 'buts' into consideration, that my machine was genuine and would continuously produce a net upward thrust in defiance of gravity.

By the time the report had been completed and submitted to BWN, Janet and I were back again in Dundee for another spell at home. A copy of the twenty-three-page document reached me at the end of March. The front page was prominently headed 'Confidential', below which was the title 'Measurement of Force Generation of a Prototype Gyroscope Invention'. Noel Carroll had made it clear that the contents were not to be divulged for public consumption at that stage. This was just as frustrating for me as it was for Ron Thompson. With the media breathing down my neck for the latest progress report on the machine, I now had to pretend that the tests had not yet taken place while all the time we were sitting on the very evidence that proved my machine was genuine.

The local paper ran a story on my return headed: 'Dundee "Anti-Gravity" Man Back in Town'. This, by the way, has always remained my favourite headline. In it I was quoted: 'I can't say too much about my work at this moment but everything is going well. There have been no hiccups and my research is bang on course. Hopefully I'll be in a position to make a more detailed announcement in a couple of months. My wife and I just had to come home to see our latest grandchild – our sixth – who was born while we were in Australia.'

This, of course, was true. One of our two daughters had added to her family in our absence and we had been forced to follow the tense build-up to this happy event on the end of a telephone. For this reason alone we had been anxious to get back to Dundee. But our real purpose for returning was to prepare the construction of another machine, one of quite a different design concept, which I had convinced Noel was the next logical step in improving the lift factor. He had agreed readily enough. He spoke to Ron Thompson himself and explained what was happening. According to Ron, Noel told him that if the new machine also gave positive results in the laboratory later that year he could release the full story of the scientific evaluation. Ron, not wishing to jeopardize my position with BWN, had been forced to agree. But he was clearly unhappy. The laboratory results were now known to quite a number of people in Australia who were privy to such information. He had this recurring nightmare that somehow there would be a leak and the story of my machine's success would break 12,000 miles away and leave him looking foolish. It was something he had to live with.

Although there could be no public disclosure of the laboratory report at this time, Thompson decided, with my approval, to submit it on a strictly confidential basis to a number of experts and ask them to evaluate its contents. He was anxious to know in advance what authoritative sources he could quote in support of the story when the document was finally released. Copies of the report were sent by prior arrangement to Professor Eric Laithwaite, Imperial College; Professor Stephen Salter, Edinburgh University; Dr Harold Aspden, Southampton University; Dr Geoffrey Pardoe, an international authority on space technology, formerly chief engineer at Hawker Siddeley and now chairman of the Watt Committee on Energy; and Professor Allan Barr, head of the Engineering Department, Aberdeen University.

Professors Laithwaite and Salter had both seen my original machine in action and were familiar with the project. Dr Aspden was following my progress closely and we had by then held a meeting at Heathrow Airport during a brief stop-over on my last trip to Australia. Dr Pardoe had been recommended by the Advanced Energy Research Institute to whom he acted as one of their advisors. Professor Barr had considerable experience of gyroscopes and was known personally to Ron Thompson.

Professor Laithwaite was the only referee who didn't reply in writing. But he told Thompson on the telephone he was not surprised at the outcome of the tests because he had always believed the machine was genuine. However, he felt I still didn't fully understand how the forces were being created and until I did I would, possibly, be unable to improve the lift to a more convincing level. 'He hasn't cracked the problem yet,' said Laithwaite. 'He's still working by intuition.'

Professor Salter wrote: 'Both my interest and puzzlement remain unabated. My impressions of the report are that the work has been done by an efficient laboratory. The precautions taken to eliminate experimental errors seem to be sound and the statistical analysis thorough. While it would have been more convincing if a larger lift had been obtained, the production of a lift which is two per cent of the oscillating forces, when classical Newton physics predicts zero, presents a fascinating problem. The strength of the evidence would obviously be increased if Sandy Kidd can produce a stronger effect.' He said the aim should be a mathematical formula to compare with the experimental results. Then he concluded: 'Every scientific theory should be able to take a vigorous poke from time to time. I am sure that Sir Isaac would be just as interested in the experiments as I am.'

Dr Aspden harboured no doubts about the results. 'I can assure you this is an extremely important scientific breakthrough,' he wrote. 'It is certain to have major technological consequences affecting air transportation and the space exploration scene. No scientist before this gyroscope discovery could have believed it possible to produce lift forces from a self-contained apparatus devoid of jet exhausts of some kind.' The test procedure itself was beyond criticism, he said. It had been conducted by experts using equipment specially designed for the task. 'It means that the force-precessed gyroscope defies the accepted laws of physics. Physicists will insist on more and more proof. It will shake the scientific community to its very core but, more importantly, can be the basis on which to develop new methods of air transportation and even space travel with minimal energy consumption, just enough to overcome gravitation and internal friction; no hot jet loss.'

The reaction of Dr Pardoe was on a much lower key. He wrote: 'The machine has promise but I am disturbed at the marginality of the net thrusts demonstrated. This may be due to the weakness of design of the test apparatus and conditions, but I get a bit concerned that the effect is really happening when a positive conclusion depends on a probability analysis. My impression is that the device should have produced a significant thrust, easily measurable. So my first question is (not answered in the documentation) if the inventor's theories are correct, what thrust would he have expected in this test from his theoretical calculations? Then secondly, how does this compare with his results? If this test confirms his theoretical predictions, then we have a device of very low power and a long way to go before any practical application can be foreseen.'

Professor Barr was similarly cautious. He said he could only regard the case at this stage as 'not proven'. He wrote: 'To be sure that any observed "lift" was real, a very close examination of the experiment would need to be carried out, including the consideration of possible error sources both in the hardware and in the way the data was analysed. The description in the report is not sufficiently detailed to allow either of these to be estimated with any precision. However, it could be very interesting if further experiments continued to show the "lift" effect with enhanced magnitude if possible. That could take some explaining!'

It was, as I suspected it would be, a mixed bag of reaction, reflecting once more the conservative nature of the academic world. Apart from Harold Aspden the experts had preferred not to stick their heads too high above the parapet. Noel Carroll, of course, had been the same. On the other hand, even at the most pessimistic level, no one had been able to reject the results out of hand. But I was now beginning to realize that, no matter how convinced I was about the conclusive nature of the laboratory results, it was the judgement of others that would finally decide what was acceptable and what was not. That was the way the system worked. If I didn't conform I was simply going to get a very sore head indeed banging it against a wall.

Chapter 15

Within a year of my machine hitting the headlines the whole subject of inertial drive propulsion was enjoying a very definite renaissance. Gyroscopic power had once again become a fashionable topic of conversation in academic circles and beyond. The potential of spinning wheels was back on the agenda of public debate. I could tell this from my own postbag alone. Lecturers and students in universities and polytechnics were constantly asking me for more information about my project. Other letters and phone calls brought news of machine-building plans from a wide variety of people who had been so inspired by my own story that they, too, were determined to reach for the stars. For many it was a form of escapism from an otherwise uneventful existence; a romantic notion, no matter how remote, that they might somehow devise the means of getting a flying saucer into space.

There were already quite a number of inertial thrust machines scattered around the world. People had been building them for ages, the mysteries of anti-gravity having long engaged the curiosity of man. Machines are usually named after their creators as an easy means of reference in identifying their different characteristics. We have the Dean Machine, Jones Machine, Greed Machine, Russell Machine, Rickman Machine, and now, of course, the Kidd Machine, to mention but a few.

I had studied the specifications of each one but found none to be a serious threat to my own device. Nevertheless these inventors, being very protective of their own creations, were naturally on their guard when a new one like mine suddenly appeared on the horizon. They would pounce if they felt endangered, as I was soon to find out for myself. Peter Greed, the Swindon physics teacher whose invention I had first read about in *The Times*' coverage of my own machine, had not hesitated in contacting Dundee University. He had drawn their attention to the patent he had held for a gyroscopic device since 1974 and suggested that any application made for my machine could not be upheld. But when the university's patent agents secured a copy of Mr Greed's patent it was discovered that my machine differed sufficiently in design from his as to justify the possibility of another patent being granted.

Then a British Telecom technician, Geoffrey Russell, of Orpington, Kent, lodged a complaint with the Press Council against the *Daily Mail*, alleging that the newspaper had inaccurately attributed the scientific discovery and invention of gyroscopic propulsion to me whereas, he claimed, he was the proprietor and inventor of the first gyroscopic propulsion system patented in September, 1983. When investigating the complaint, the Press Council took evidence from the reporter involved who said he had received more letters about the Sandy Kidd story than any other he had ever written. Finally the Press Council rejected the complaint against the *Daily Mail*, stating in its adjudication:

> It is not inconceivable or particularly unusual for two people working independently to make the same, or similar, scientific discoveries. This appears to have happened in this case. It was not improper for the *Daily Mail* to publish a story about the invention by Mr Kidd, of which it knew, and there was no obligation on it to publish another story about Mr Russell's patented invention when he drew this to the paper's notice. Notwithstanding Mr Russell's letters, the paper was entitled to publish its second story about Mr Kidd's invention. Any question of patent rights is not one for the Press Council. The complaint against the *Daily Mail* is rejected.

I later learned that Geoffrey Russell had won an epic struggle in gaining his patent. Originally the examiner of his application had ruled that, because the invention was considered to violate established natural laws and was therefore incapable of industrial application as required under Section One of the 1977 Patents Act, a patent could not be granted. Russell, however, had a machine that worked and although he was never able to find a backer for its development he had successfully demonstrated his device to a number of experts whose evidence he then produced in support of his patent application.

In handling the Russell appeal, the Patent Office was faced with a difficult dilemma. Russell had a machine. The machine had been seen to produce a force. But the explanation of how this had been achieved appeared to be contrary to the whole basis of Newtonian physics. In the end the superintending examiner wrote in his report:

' . . . I have grave doubts, both from a theoretical and a practical standpoint, as to whether the invention as at present described and claimed is such as to warrant the grant of a patent. Nevertheless, I am faced with evidence from three reputable sources to the effect that the applicant has produced an apparatus (the construction of which is apparently consistent with the basic teaching of the application in suit) which they consider is capable of moving its own centre of mass. In such circumstances, I consider that it would not be right to refuse the application at this early stage, and I therefore propose to allow the proceedings to resume their normal course.' Twenty months later Russell was granted his patent. Perhaps, however, this was the sort of problem I would be faced with myself when my application came under closer scrutiny at a later stage.

Although I was fairly certain I was ahead of the field with the design of a machine which had been laboratory tested, there was another inventor coming up fast on the outside lane who was causing me a bit of concern. He was also a Scotsman, Scott Strachan, who lived only sixty miles away from Dundee in my native city of Edinburgh. He had phoned me at the time my own machine had been made public to tell me about a device he had made himself. His was one of dozens of calls arising from the television programme and I thought little more about our conversation. Then, just over a year later in June 1988, his name cropped up again, this time in connection with a prestigious event being staged in Ottawa, Canada. This was the Third International New Energy Technology Symposium and Exhibition at which distinguished scientists and engineers would be delivering a wide range of papers on power sources of the future.

I had actually received an invitation to speak and demonstrate my machine at the seminar which, in the new climate of inertial thrust popularity, had a whole section devoted to gyroscopic machines. But at the time I was hard at work assembling and testing another device at Mark Beran's place in Boulder, Colorado, and was unable to go. Scott Strachan, however, had accepted a similar invitation to attend and the demonstration he gave of his machine had caused a mild sensation. Harold Aspden, who had been a speaker at the seminar, told me about the Strachan Machine when he returned home.

Like mine, it consisted of two gyros on a crossarm under force precession with a cam at the top of the central shaft. Aspden said the machine had produced a one-pound thrust against a counterweight and he had been greatly impressed by its performance. There was no doubt it resembled my device much more than any of the others and it caused me to sit up and take notice. When someone accomplishes something along the same lines as yourself one's curiosity lies not only in what they have achieved but also in what sort of person they are. The story behind Scott Strachan is certainly fascinating. He is a professional inventor who operates his business from a wheelchair.

Like myself Scott never went to university for an academic training. He was a 'hands on' man from the very start, although he attended night school and day release courses to take his Higher National certificates in applied physics and chemistry and electrical engineering. By that time he was a design engineer working for a medical physics company in the new town of Livingston, thirty miles from Edinburgh, where he was involved in the development of ultra-sonic scanners. Even then, before he had reached the age of twenty, it was obvious he had a remarkably inventive mind. He was a boffin right down to his bootstraps. He went on to specialize in acoustics, wave theory and optics, starting up his own business in 1978 as an inventor. When clients weren't coming to him with problems to solve he went out to identify needs in the scientific marketplace, then applied his innovative mind to filling these gaps. He tackled anything and everything: measuring instruments for the medical professional, an advanced hi-fi pick-up arm, the development of a bulk manufacturing process for a new plastic piezoelectric material. All these new ideas have given him a portfolio of over thirty patents and a considerable reputation as a very bright young man. He is still only thirty-two.

He has been interested in gyros all his life. His grandparents in Ayr always had a box of toy gyros in the house which he played with as a youngster. The waywardness of these spinning wheels continued to fascinate him right through his youth until he, too, fell under the spell of Eric Laithwaite's Christmas lectures of 1974. Like me, he had sat in front of his television set spellbound by what the professor had been able to do with his gyroscopes on that occasion, almost like a circus ringmaster putting jungle animals through a series of tricks. These demonstrations had the same impact on both our minds and from that moment, unknown to each other of course, the paths we followed bore an uncanny resemblance.

Scott, like myself, began to dabble in his own experiments with a view to building a gyroscopic propulsion machine. But he got his act together more quickly than I did and by 1981 had completed his first device in his own workshop in Edinburgh. The machine, just as I was to build later, consisted of two gyros on a crossarm with a vertical shaft which had a camshaft fitted to the top end. There was also a counterweight system but his was operated on what is called a parallel balance. This is a shaft placed horizontally on a bench with the counterweight at one end and the machine fixed to the other where it hangs vertically below the shaft as it protrudes over the end of the worktop.

The device weighed sixteen pounds and was soon producing a lift equal to two pounds, much the same percentage as my first machine three years later. Strachan contacted Professor Laithwaite and was duly invited down to Imperial College for a demonstration. Everything went splendidly. The machine put on its best performance and the professor, along with several of his colleagues, appeared to be impressed. But that was it. Scott returned to Edinburgh to think out his next step. He believed that a parity machine, capable in effect of lifting itself off the ground, was what he had to aim for. 'In those days there weren't the same openings for a partial-effect machine,' he says. 'It had to be all or nothing. Things are different now with satellites, for example, capable of being driven in space by a gyroscopic propulsion unit producing a comparatively modest thrust.' The Edinburgh inventor then built a machine in which the gyros, instead of being controlled by a cam, were allowed to 'fly' continuously at will. But he soon found, as I did with my second machine, that such an arrangement simply didn't work and you finish up with no lift at all. He then gave up and, with his own business beginning to blossom, put gyroscopes to the back of his mind.

In 1986 Scott's life took a tragic turn when he was thrown from his horse during a cross-country event near Edinburgh. His injuries that day rendered him a paraplegic and committed him to a wheelchair for the rest of his life. For a young man who was a promising cricketer and a keen horseman his perspective of life changed overnight. A great many things were now beyond his reach for ever. But his brain was unimpaired and so were his hands. He could see no reason why he shouldn't continue to run his business from a wheelchair and that is what he has courageously done ever since.

Then, on May 22, 1987, the day my story first broke in the newspapers, Scott found himself once again caught up in the tangle of spinning wheels. When he arrived at his office that morning he was greeted by a colleague who announced mysteriously, 'Well, I see you've been beaten to it.' Scott was puzzled. Then it was explained to him how a Dundee engineer had successfully built the same sort of gyroscopic machine that he had abandoned several years before. Strachan grabbed the newspapers and was amazed to read how I had followed in his footsteps, ending up at Imperial College.

'When I read the story I had mixed feelings,' he told me. 'I was naturally disappointed that I hadn't persisted in improving my own machine and maintaining my lead. But I was also delighted that someone else had overcome all the problems I had faced with my first device and had succeeded in finding university support.'

Scott decided to get back into the race. But rather than reverting to his original machine, he developed a simple piece of test equipment which he called the Strachan Experiment. This was a neat bit of apparatus consisting of a single gyro and powered by electric motors. It demonstrated in a simplified but measurable way the principle of inertial thrust as exhibited in a full-scale device. Five months later, in October that year, he took the test unit through to Strathclyde University in Glasgow where he was involved in development work on a flexible mirror project. Leonard Holihan, representing the Advanced Energy Research Institute, along with Dr Geoffrey Pardoe, who acted as one of their advisors, were also to be there and he wanted to run his experiment for their benefit. He linked up his device to a set of wheels and let it roll across the floor to demonstrate the thrust being produced by the gyros. Both men were immediately interested and suggested that he build a machine that could produce a force equal to ten per cent of its weight. They appeared to indicate that such a measurement of anti-gravity thrust would be convincing enough to attract development funding.

Strachan's first machine already performed to that level. Now he built another on the same principle,but to a more streamlined design, bringing the weight down from sixteen pounds to ten pounds. This gave him a one-pound thrust, the ten per cent of the static weight asked for, with other runs achieving nearly twice that lift but only at the risk of damaging the machine because of the stress factors involved. The institute followed up this promising performance by inviting him to the Ottawa seminar which they themselves were helping to sponsor. Strachan told me about his Canadian experience with some amusement.

On the night before his demonstration lecture he ran his machine successfully in his hotel bedroom before a private audience of half a dozen delegates. He thought the preview might help to stimulate a lively dialogue at his session the following day. It did nothing of the sort. 'Nearly one hundred and thirty delegates watched my device produce impressive amounts of inertial thrust but none of them questioned the integrity of the machine or the accuracy of the measurements,' he said. 'Their apparent acceptance of this highly controversial piece of evidence completely floored me. I had been ready to defend my corner against a barrage of criticism. Instead I had to waffle on about the consequences of all this for the future of science without any opposition. I somehow felt cheated.'

Since the Ottawa seminar in June, 1988, Strachan has been visited by various academic figures and funding bodies but so far no one has taken his machine under their wing. He, himself, remains fairly philosophical about the whole business. He believes that gyroscopic propulsion will eventually become a reality but not until the force factor is of an order which the Establishment simply cannot ignore. Like me he is certain that gyros have the intrinsic ability to change the world if only we can maximize their potential as an energy source. 'The answer definitely lies within these spinning wheels,' he says. 'But so far none of us have discovered the full truth.'

Scott firmly believes that he and I have already developed devices with enough thrust for certain commercial uses, particularly as a drive unit for satellites operating in space where you don't have to overcome gravity and friction. He reckons that his machine as it stands is eighty times more powerful than the ion drive used for satellites and is only a fifth of the weight. The trouble is it would break up under the strain. A more efficient propulsion system is only viable at the end of the day if it can last at least as long as existing technology. This, however, could be achieved by using certain materials. As Scott says, it's all possible if those with the money and influence have got the courage to back the future.

Strachan is in favour of collaboration with someone like myself in making the final push for the finishing line. He believes that we should get round a table, 'spill out our brains', and build a device between us. 'Both of us have now reached the stage,' he says, 'where we should be working together to save duplication of effort in solving the same problems.' But he recognizes the difficulty, as I do, of two inventors pooling their ideas after ploughing lonely furrows with considerable success. There is always the fear that before a proper joint

143

agreement can be drawn up one of the parties will make a remark of technical significance which the other will promptly incorporate into his machine and then claim the credit for a breakthrough.

To overcome this risk Scott offered to have any preliminary meeting between us tape-recorded by a third party so that in the event of such a thing happening the source of the idea could always be properly established. But I had no hesitation in turning down Strachan's proposal of marriage between my machine and his. What did I have to gain by such a union? I already had the financial backing of a top development company. My machine had been scientifically approved and I was pretty certain I was heading in the right direction. I realized at some stage the maths men would have to move in and work out the formula of what the machine was doing. The help of specialist engineers would also be needed to help me improve the physique and output of the device. But as far as the conceptualization was concerned, I preferred to stick to my own ideas and back my own hunches. Put it down to arrogance if you wish, but I honestly believed I could carry on and finish off the groundwork myself.

Chapter 16

How did my machine really work? What was actually taking place within that whirling mass of metal? What forces were at play creating the magical thrust which was openly defying the laws of physics? Were the gyros moving in and up and then out again in a straightforward path or were they following some devious route in building up their energy? No one could answer any of these questions with absolute certainty. The chemistry of my machine was still largely a matter of conjecture. I had my own theories, of course, but these were subject to constant fine tuning as the machine itself took on different design characteristics.

If I was being honest, Professor Laithwaite's verdict that I was working by intuition had a certain ring of truth to it. Someone else had likened me to a high handicap golfer who one day shot a 64 then spent the rest of his life trying to find out what he had done right. But I simply had to keep on going forward in search of the truth, whether by intuition, instinct or inspiration.

One alternative was to throw up my arms in defeat and walk away from what I had created. That was unthinkable. No, the only way to really understand the anatomy of my machine was to assemble a team of experts with all the latest technology to break down and analyse each of its movements on a test rig and then construct a formula which would give a mathematical explanation for everything that was happening. Having achieved all that we could then decide from the hard evidence of fact and not guesswork what had to be done next to improve the principle of gyroscopic propulsion.

This had been the plan of action in Dundee University. BWN had declared the same intention but so far had not taken the plunge. It was, however, a big step to take. Laboratory work didn't come cheaply. The cost of putting a machine through a three-day proving programme was nothing compared to months of painstaking research and analysis at a specialist level. But at what point did you commit yourself to the big-spending league? We now had a machine which had been proved to have the seeds of success. In many ways this was the time to launch the concerted team effort. I realized that in the foreseeable future I would have to stand back and allow others to take over the Kidd Machine and shape its future in much the same way as a doting parent must relinquish the monopoly of their child at school age. But, despite understanding the logic of all this, I still wanted to build one more machine, test one other theory, before calling in the cavalry.

For some time now, even as I had been building my first machine in Australia, I had been thinking ahead to the shape of things to come. I knew that to create substantial thrust, not merely a handful of ounces in a partial-effect machine, I required a device quite different to anything else that had gone before. I was now certain that my machine's success depended on what happened to the gyros' angular momentum. According to physics this always remains constant and conserved in a rotating body. I, however, now contended that my gyros were losing some of their angular momentum as they moved in towards the machine's central shaft during precession and then regaining it as they were slammed back out by centrifugal force to release their vertical thrust. But if the gyros could lose and then regain a larger measure of this momentum more quickly, then I was convinced I would get much more thrust. I was sure the answer lay in the speed and impact of change in the state of the gyros. This virtually meant stopping and starting the gyros continuously during rotation, while at the same time making them move in and out more rapidly than with the eccentrics or camshaft.

A special mechanism would have to be built into the gyros themselves to make them self-oscillating. Wheels couldn't be adapted to do this. But balls could. They would be hollow spheres able to carry the components I had in mind. Balls as gyros. It had, of course, been done before but never in this way. My angular momentum theory had the support of Harold Aspden. In the notes accompanying his evaluation of my laboratory report he had written:

> As every engineer knows machines keep a perfect energy balance. They never get 'in the red'. If they absorb energy in one form they invariably deploy that energy by putting it into a new useful form, storing it in some way, or expelling it as by heat discharge into the atmosphere. The governing law of science is the 'Principle of Energy Conservation'. It is a

146

law that is never breached. Engineers also live with two other principles which derive from Newtonian mechanics. Angular momentum and linear momentum are separately conserved. The momentum of a body is its mass times its speed, the angular speed being applicable for angular momentum. Our machines depend upon this conservative action and it would shake the very foundations of science if any one of the conservation rules was proved erroneous. The wheel of a car never begins to turn without pushing against the earth in a way that affects the rotation of body Earth to keep that angular momentum balance. A shell fired from a gun gives a kick-back which is absorbed by the earth to cause body Earth itself to adjust its momentum in the opposite direction to keep overall balance, the earth readjusting as the shell strikes its earthly target. If the earth momentarily acquires angular momentum in this process, that arises because the shell at rest in the gun had angular momentum owing to its rotation with body Earth. Never, it seems, is there a breach of the conservation rules. But now the world must be prepared for a shock. Your machine has been demonstrated under rigorous test conditions to breach these sacrosanct conservation rules.

It was comforting to know I wasn't alone in the wilderness with my theories as I poured out all these thoughts on a new machine to Noel Carroll the day after completing my laboratory trials in Melbourne. I was even able to show him some preliminary drawings. He seemed impressed, realizing this was no spur-of-the-moment gimmick but a device which had been carefully thought out. He readily agreed to go along with my plan of action. I would return home to Scotland immediately and have the machine made by a high-precision engineering company near Dundee whose work I knew from previous experience would be reliable and delivered on time. The machine I had designed – prototype Mark 6 – would be the first to have four gyros instead of two. Each ball, four inches in diameter, would be an aluminium hollow sphere fitted into its own cradle at the end of a crossarm. These four gyro arms would be intersected by the machine's main vertical shaft. As previously, the gyros and the device would rotate separately. The gyros would operate in pairs, first one set and then another oscillating in and out in rapid succession. The total weight of the machine would be eighteen pounds. It would be eight inches tall with an overall diameter of twenty inches. It would rotate at 250 rpm with the balls capable of spinning at 4000 rpm.

During the next two months, while the device gradually took shape at the hands of skilled engineers using computerized technology, Janet and I had expected to relax a little in preparation for our next stint in Australia. Instead, I found myself suddenly caught up in an episode of high drama which ended in the Kidd Machine becoming the subject of discussion at United Nations level in Switzerland. This all stemmed from the protracted negotiations over transferring the patent rights of my machine from Dundee University to BWN.

The university had said from the start they would be prepared to assign their interest in the invention to the Australian company in return for payment of the £8000 they had invested in their aborted project. BWN had made it equally clear that their agreement with me was conditional on acquiring these rights, dated from December 9, 1986, the date on which the university's patent application had first been filed at the Patent Office in London. This was known as the priority date. It was from that day my machine was initially protected, making it vital, therefore, that BWN secured this backdated protection to prevent them being frozen out by another similar invention for which a patent might have been applied for since the filing of the initial application. But in December, 1987, the Australian company told the university they would assume the patent rights on the basis that the compensation would be paid sometime within the following twelve months. In the absence of such payment the rights would be assigned back to the university. BWN said they wanted more time to assess the viability of the invention. This, of course, was before my machine had gone through the laboratory. The university said these terms were quite unacceptable and contrary to what they believed had been agreed in principle. They were simply not prepared to hand over the goods on approval. They had to be paid cash on delivery.

The outcome of this long and difficult bargaining session was deadlock. Neither party was prepared to give ground. BWN then proceeded unilaterally to file an international patent application for my Australian machine in the name of Noel Carroll and myself and in doing so claimed the priority date of the university application. They did this on December 9, 1987, exactly one year after the original application and the last possible day for taking such action. While the patent agents in Melbourne worked feverishly to complete and despatch the documentation in time, the scene 12,000 miles away was also one of mounting tension. The university's patent agent, Dr Robert Naismith, shivering in his dressing gown, was pacing the floor of his house in the west of Scotland at two o'clock on a cold winter's morning trying to establish on the telephone with his counterpart in Melbourne if BWN were to go ahead with an application. By seven o'clock that same morning a bleary-eyed Dr Naismith reached his office in the centre of Glasgow to find a message from Australia waiting for him on his fax machine. It was then he learned that BWN had taken the plunge.

It was now the turn of Dr Naismith and his staff to start their race against the clock as they, too, nine hours in time behind Australia, prepared an international patent application for the Dundee machine to safeguard the position of the university. This was really an extension of their original application and naturally it was also based on the earlier filing date. What we now had was two applications for what was basically the same invention. At that stage the dispute took off.

The university lodged an official complaint with the World Intellectual Property Organization in Geneva. WIPO, as it is known, is one of the sixteen specialized bodies of the United Nations who act as watchdogs over international arrangements relating to patents, copyright and trade marks. They are responsible for promoting the protection of intellectual property (a high-sounding phrase for ideas) throughout the world by inter-state co-operation. The objection claimed that the Australian application had usurped the rights of Dundee University. Their agent argued that two applications for the same invention could not co-exist and in the circumstances BWN's application should be cancelled.

WIPO wasted no time in responding. Within a week their legal section had neatly sidestepped the dispute by ruling that a patent application at this stage was made in confidence and they were unable to discuss either its merits or declare it inadmissible. The ruling ended: 'Legal action should in such a case be taken in the country where the application was filed or in the designated states, according to the applicable national law.'

The dispute, however, was finally resolved in an amicable fashion, but the Australians waited on the successful outcome of the laboratory tests before clinching the deal. The university's share of the patent rights were duly assigned with my approval and BWN paid cash on the nail. At that stage the university ceased to have an interest in the application. Once again I found myself hardly able to believe that such events were taking place as a result of my machine. Letters, phone calls and facsimile messages had been flashing round the world, involving high-powered attorneys and officials of a United Nations agency. For something that had come out of a humble garden shed the Kidd Machine was moving in rarefied circles.

By the middle of May all the parts of my new device had been made. As they arrived from the factory I had been storing them in the house with the same reverence as for the family jewels. Janet couldn't quite understand this affectionate attitude towards bits and pieces of silicon aluminium. But when I assembled the machine loosely on our coffee table in the lounge she had a better appreciation of my enthusiasm for this new device. It really did look impressive, a different shape altogether from the previous prototypes. This one was low and flat, almost like a mechanical spider, with a mass of linkages, arms and shafts leading out from the centre until reaching the big, gleaming hollow spheres sitting in their cradles at the four corners of the machine. The balls seemed to dominate everything else, bringing a touch of mystery to this latest anti-gravity creation. They certainly held the key to its success.

Having satisfied myself that the components were up to specification I contacted BWN and told them I was ready for the next stage of the programme. There had never been any intention that I should assemble and run the machine in Dundee prior to it entering the Melbourne laboratory. I presumed all the preparatory work was going to take place at the factory in Dandenong. But Noel Carroll told me to proceed once again to Colorado and run the machine in under the watchful eye of Mark Beran before moving on to Australia. This suited Janet and me fine. Boulder in the spring would be a delight.

This would be our fourth round-the-world trip in less than a year. By now we were resigned to shooting backwards and forwards between all these far-flung destinations, packing and unpacking, and settling into different routines to fit the lifestyles of the various countries. This time our luggage included the dismantled parts of the new machine, split up into plastic packages and stuffed away among all the new clothing we would require for the onset of the Australian winter.

In due course I turned up at Mark's workshop in Niwot with a case containing all my latest wares, feeling more like a travelling salesman than an inventor about to take another step into the unknown. Over the next few weeks we worked away patiently, first assembling the components and then gradually breaking in the finished machine with a variable-speed electric motor. By June 24 we were ready to run the device flat out to achieve lift. We waited until the cool of evening before getting everything under way. The machine responded positively against the counterweight from the very start and before that night was out we knew it was producing a good measurement of lift. It was averaging out at one and a half pounds or just below ten per cent of the machine's weight. Mark and I were obviously delighted. The system seemed to be working according to plan. That night we celebrated on his verandah under the starry skies of Colorado. A few days later a fax from Noel Carroll summoned me to Australia to prepare the machine for its laboratory examination sometime in July.

At Dandenong, Janet and I moved back again into our bungalow at Endeavour Hills, glad to revert to a normal domestic life after four weeks of hotel existence in Boulder. When you stay in a hotel for that length of time you are aware of the constant coming and going of other guests while you linger on in this rootless sort of environment. For homebirds like us it was all rather unsettling.

My first days back at the BWN factory were spent assembling the machine once again after its promising debut in Colorado. I then drove it down to the VIPAC technology centre at Port Melbourne to discuss the test arrangements with John Simmons and his staff. They could foresee no problems in putting the device through the same procedure as before. This time, however, the fuel and water tanks would be kept apart from the hanging box with supplies fed in by external lines. This would keep down the overall weight of the unit and give me a better percentage of lift in the final analysis. It would also allow the machine to run for longer spells with unlimited fuel and water available, instead of the restricted supplies we had previously carried on board. As before, I was going to power the gyros and the device with an internal combustion engine but on this occasion the gears would be made of plastic to allow me to control the speeds with a radio control unit.

Everything went smoothly enough as I worked steadily on into my first Australian winter, anxious to have the machine ready in its box for the test date which had been fixed for July 21. When everything was finally completed on time the total unit weighed twenty-eight pounds. The routine at the laboratory was the same as before with the box being hung from a gantry at the end of a Kevlar cord. This time, of course, Janet and I were familiar with the environment. But this did little to quell my anxiety over the testing of a machine which was so different in design from any of its predecessors. I was also disturbed by the fact that the device had never reproduced its Colorado form in Australia. Although still lifting on the bench, it had been failing to give the same thrust as we got initially in Mark's workshop. Its inconsistent behaviour had me puzzled. Nevertheless, I was unprepared for the catalogue of mishaps which turned the first test day into a nightmare.

The machine broke down continually with fractured shafts, engine failure, fuel seepage and, to add insult to injury, a faulty silencer. Two partially completed runs were all we accomplished on a day I prefer to forget. That night, back at the factory in Dandenong, I worked feverishly to repair the damage in time for a fresh start the following day. When I turned up at the laboratory in the morning I was bleary-eyed through lack of sleep.

Day two was also a write-off. This time the ball joints kept shearing. I was filled with despair. The forces being produced by the machine were creating a massive reaction within the framework of the device, causing problems through stress and fatigue. The concept of the balls was certainly working and they were creating plenty of thrust. You could almost feel the machine throbbing with pent-up energy. But it seemed to be unable to realease these powerful pulses in a single positive force. At the end of that second day I was pacing about in my workshop, licking my wounds and wondering which way to turn next. I felt terribly lonely and would have given anything to be back in my own garden shed in Dundee. But I forced myself to concentrate on the problem that now faced me. I realized there was something basically wrong with my machine which no amount of tinkering was going to cure. Certain structural alterations would have to be carried out on the design. Over the next few days I decided what these should be, then told Noel I wanted to return to Scotland to place the work in the hands of the same engineering company who had made the machine. He agreed.

Janet and I arrived back in Scotland on August 5 to be met by friends at Edinburgh Airport and driven the last part of our journey home to Dundee. As we motored north across the Forth Road Bridge I couldn't help but compare our homecoming with our previous return from Australia five months earlier. Then we had been on top of the world, conquering heroes fresh from success in the first laboratory trials. Now we were back with a sick machine and little to celebrate. Such are the fluctuating fortunes of the innovator. There is a maxim for inventors which says that you must never become too elated at success or too dispirited with failure. How true. But

152

there is no denying that a failed mission makes your jet lag seem a lot worse.

Defeat, however, was far from my thoughts as I got to work on the detailed drawings for the modifications. These affected the sizes and angles of certain shafts and I was fairly confident the changes would get me back on the rails once again. Four weeks later I headed back to Australia with the revamped machine. This time I went alone. Janet had grown tired of the constant upheaval and travelling and decided she wanted a settled spell with our daughters and grandchildren. I was going to miss her moral support. But on the other hand Janet's absence would allow me to work longer hours on the machine without having to worry about her sitting alone at home in what was still largely a strange country to us both.

Back in Dandenong I began to run the machine once more and although the results were more encouraging they still weren't measuring up to what I had first achieved in Colorado. But at least the machine was now withstanding the fierce forces to which it was being subjected. After spending three more weeks making various adjustments, the device went back into the laboratory at Port Melbourne at the end of September. During the first two days each run by the machine registered a downward negative thrust only, just as the previous device had done at the start of its trials. Once again I was forced to retire hurt to my workshop at BWN.

By now I realized there were things happening inside the machine which I simply didn't know about. The answer lay somewhere within the mechanism itself. If only machines could talk! The most I could hope for was a positive result of a low order. That I felt would be enough to justify a further stage of research and development. On October 10 the machine came good at last. On its final visit to the laboratory it scored five positive results out of five runs. Although the thrust measurement was small compared to the previous results, it was genuine anti-gravity. When the laboratory staff confirmed this I experienced an overwhelming sense of relief. It meant I was heading in the right direction after all.

On the following day I had a vital meeting at the factory with Noel Carroll to discuss the future of the project. During all my problems with the latest machine he had been most supportive and encouraging, giving me a free hand to take whatever steps I thought necessary to overcome the teething difficulties of the new device. Now, as we were joined by his brother Bob who had flown in from California, he seemed anxious to set the course ahead. We all agreed that the results obtained so far from the two Australian machines had furnished us with some of the evidence we were looking for. The second device had certainly performed far short of its potential but, nevertheless, we were edging forward all the time in what, after all, was a no-man's-land in science.

I was aware that BWN were about to open new laboratories near their plant at Pasadena, just outside Los Angeles. This was an important centre in the American aerospace industry with the Californian Institute of Technology and the government's Jet Propulsion Laboratory, part of the NASA organization, already located in the area. Having stayed in Pasadena several times on our way out to Australia, Janet and I certainly favoured living in that part of the world. It had all the class that goes with a high standard of living. But more importantly, it could offer all the high technology backup we would need for a full-scale analysis of my machines.

The Carroll brothers were well aware of these advantages. Such a decision, however, could not be taken lightly. This was the big plunge. Moving the project to California would involve BWN in big bucks. But I was convinced after my latest experience with the new machine that the time had arrived for others to become involved if progress on a realistic time-scale was going to be achieved. There now seemed no other logical way forward. Noel and Bob appeared to agree with me and the decision was taken to transfer the next critical stage of development to the west coast of America, to the Golden State whose motto appropriately enough was 'Eureka'.

California, here I come! Or so I thought.

Chapter 17

When I arrived back in Dundee once again in the middle of
October 1988, I told Janet we would possibly be out in film-star
land before the end of that year. The question of a house still had
to be resolved but apart from that there seemed to be no serious
impediment to the move out West. But there was another, quite
different, problem that had to be dealt with right away.

During my recent absences from Scotland Ron Thompson had
continued to hold the Press at bay over the latest progress report
on my work. He had kept faith with Noel Carroll's request eight
months earlier to make no public announcement about the successful outcome of the laboratory tests. But Ron now told me he could
no longer suppress the facts, particularly in view of my impending
departure to California. 'This is a running story and people have a
certain right to know what is happening,' he said. 'But even without
that obligation the laboratory story standing on its own is far too
momentous to be forgotten about.'

Noel had promised Ron that he could release the laboratory news
provided my latest machine was also proved to be positive. Well,
that had happened, albeit not spectacularly. But when Thompson
phoned Australia for the go-ahead to break the story Noel said he
still did not want any disclosure. The corroborative evidence, of the
new machine, he said, had only been marginal and there was still
not sufficient proof that my device was all I was claiming it to be.
He said that BWN had a sound reputation for good judgement and
he repeated his fear of being seen to back a loser if my anti-gravity
machine finally fell flat on its face. But Ron told him he could no
longer sit on the laboratory results and pretend they hadn't happened
when it was already known that such tests were to take place. Finally,
Noel asked him to consult brother Bob who by then was back in
Pasadena.

Bob Carroll took an even stronger stance against publication. He
said that such a step would make BWN a target for vested interests

anxious to muscle in on the invention. Before they knew what was happening other companies, encouraged by the laboratory results, would be churning out machines of their own and perhaps overtaking BWN. There could even be the risk of industrial espionage. When Thompson again tried to argue his case, Bob countered by using Noel's argument about premature disclosure. 'Let's wait until we know beyond doubt that Sandy's machine has got legs,' he said. By 'legs' he had meant 'going places'. When Bob asked for an assurance of no publicity Ron refused to give it. Although he had sympathy for the company's point of view, he said that in the circumstances he had an even greater obligation to publish.

When Thompson told me about the outcome of these conversations I realized I was in a very difficult position. I had loyalty to both BWN and Ron Thompson. How could I discharge my duty to each without angering the other? After much agonizing I decided to steer a middle course. We would announce the success of the laboratory tests, quoting Dr Aspden and Professor Salter in support, but we would not release the statistical evidence contained within the main body of the report. We would describe how the tests were conducted, the number of runs completed, and the size of lift achieved. But no more. The identity of BWN, VIPAC, and the location within California of the next stage of development would not be disclosed. Technical details of the machine itself would also remain confidential. Having mulled over all this for days, my mind was finally made up when I learned through Thompson that an article written by Harold Aspden for a technical magazine on the anti-gravity properties of the force-precessed gyroscope was being published shortly. In his piece he was highlighting the Scott Strachan machine as demonstrated at the Ottawa seminar the previous year. In view of this impending publication there was no way I could hang back any longer with the success story of my own machine.

The news was carried exclusively on the front page of the *Sunday Express* on October 23 under the headline 'Scots Genius Heads for the Stars'. In the story Aspden was quoted as saying: 'It will totally revolutionize the travel industry. Taken to the ultimate, we will have planes without jet engines and helicopters without rotor blades.' Professor Laithwaite told the newspaper: 'I have always been convinced it could be done and I would like to see someone defeat the system. He may be a long time perfecting it but I am sure he will succeed.' At BWN someone identified only as a spokesman said: 'We are on to something really big. The next stage is to power up Sandy's device in California with the prospect of building a full-scale vehicle at the end of the day. Money is no object, but we are determined that his work will not get out. We are very concerned about industrial espionage. The Japanese would just love to get their hands on this.' On the centre page of the paper the *Express* also ran a leader headed 'Garden Shed Dream'. It said:

> Engineer Sandy Kidd had an idea. An amazing, unbelievable idea that defied the known laws of physics and pointed towards an entirely new form of space-age transport. So he went down to his garden shed in Dundee to think about it. And for five years he made drawings and built models there. And today? Today Sandy Kidd's theory of gyroscopic propulsion has burst upon the scientific establishment like an H-bomb. Millions of dollars are being spent in research. Eminent physicists are talking of thirty-four-hour trips to Mars, of aircraft without jet engines and helicopters without rotor blades. Isn't it wonderful that in this impersonal age of bureaucracy, it still takes only one dreamer, one dream and one garden shed to change the world?

Over the next few days follow-up stories were carried extensively in all branches of the media. On the BBC's top morning radio programme 'Today' I was interviewed along with Professor Salter and the BBC's own science correspondent David Whitehouse. Salter said he could find no mistakes in the report and yet what was being claimed was entirely contrary to classical physics. He simply couldn't explain it although he had a great respect for Sir Isaac Newton. If, however, the laboratory statistics were accepted there would have to be a considerable recasting of the Third Law to make everything else that was based on it still fit. 'This is a great puzzle,' added the professor. 'If you can show that this law is not right it is certainly worth a Nobel Prize.' He explained how, when he had tried to get others better qualified than himself in this branch of engineering to examine the report, they were so convinced that such a concept was impossible they wouldn't even read it. 'I think that's a bit sad,' reflected the professor.

David Whitehouse said that initially he had been very sceptical about the reported results, although he had not seen the report himself. Newton's Third Law had served mankind well and this would appear to be the first example of that law not being universally true, even though it was true most of the time in most places.

'What he has done is to connect up two gyros together and get an additional force which cannot be explained. Now, at the moment, I find that absolutely fascinating and if it is true this could be very revolutionary indeed.' Then Whitehouse sounded words of caution, adding: 'I won't really believe it until we have more data. The data we have at the moment is not very extensive. It is highly secret and until it is published in a scientific journal, and other people reproduce the same effect and better minds than mine look at it and say it really cannot be explained, I won't really believe it. At the moment I am interested but not convinced.'

In the *Daily Star* Brian Hitchen devoted most of his weekly column to a hard-hitting piece on the timidity of Britain's banks in backing new ideas. Under the heading 'Too Scared to Gamble' this is part of what he wrote:

> If Sir Francis Drake or Christopher Columbus had been shopping for venture capital in Britain today much of the world might have gone undiscovered. For when it comes to taking a gamble on a brand new invention, are not some British bankers a lot of old women? Latest victim of Britain's fiscal timidity is Mr Sandy Kidd, fifty-one-year-old former apprentice toolmaker whose invention is so revolutionary that it may wind up knocking Isaac Newton's Law of Motion right out of the text books. It threatens to change the face of travel. Day trips to Australia and a ride along the Milky Way could become a reality. Mars would be only thirty-four hours away. And on a journey from London to Sydney there wouldn't be time for a cup of coffee . . . That for Britain is the good news. Surely the bad news is that Mr Kidd is hopping off to California and will now complete his work there. Sponsored by an Australian research company. And why? Because some British bankers were too unimaginative to put their money behind a man who worked out of a garden shed in Dundee for five years. So yet another British invention will be manufactured overseas – and, like television, no doubt will be sold back to us. Do they not know that from such fanciful threads are dreams woven? Or are bankers only brave enough to back something that can be repossessed if their 'investment' looks a bit dodgy? . . . Tragically Mr Kidd won't be the last inventor to wind up in a foreign camp because bankers dither so – or want such a big piece of the action that there is hardly anything left for the genius who

dreamed it up. From his laboratory Mr Kidd said: 'Nobody was willing to take a chance. I'm sad Britain didn't back me.' So am I, Mr Kidd, so am I.

Noel Carroll soon found out about all this coverage when the foreign editions of the British papers reached Australia. But Thompson had also faxed him an explanation of what he had done, why he had done it, and offered to send him an advance copy of the Aspden article spotlighting the Strachan Machine, the forewarning of which had finally clinched our decision to publish on a limited basis. Noel sent back a curt acknowledgement: 'Dear Ron, I hear what you say and now it's done. Let us forget it and when we really have something to rave about, we can sing Sandy's praises.'

So, there! I had received my comeuppance from my Australian paymasters. What I couldn't tell was whether Noel's put-down of my machine was the way he really felt about it or simply a deliberate attempt to lay a false trail for competing interests. What he didn't seem to realize from his distant base was the way in which the whole subject of gyroscopic propulsion had taken off in Britain as a result of the Kidd Machine. It was no exaggeration to say that news of the laboratory results had sent another tremor of interest right through the country. There was, of course, the usual deluge of letters and phone calls, the mixture as before of the congratulatory, the curious, and the critical.

From Bath an engineer wrote to the *Sunday Express*: 'I fear that Sandy was just "Kidding" when he gave you that story about gyroscopic propulsion. Or was the article inadvertently printed five and a half months too soon? It was just the thing for April 1.'

A lecturer in mechanical engineering at a polytechnic in the south of England said in his letter that to suggest a gyroscope could produce a force was 'a complete con on a par with a perpetual motion machine.'

Several of the correspondents were still harping on about the old bogey of aerodynamic effect. Time and again critics were suggesting, as Dr Bill Ferrier had done originally, that my machine was simply lifting on the same principle as a helicopter. From my own study of the subject I had always known this was not the case, but I now decided to nail this red herring once and for all. The person best qualified to do so was Rupert Lucas, the former helicopter expert at Rolls Royce who had previously offered to collaborate on my work. He was now a director of Turbo Kinetic

Design Ltd, a group of power engineering consultants based in Derby. Mr Lucas had not actually studied my laboratory report but he knew the machine had been in a sealed box during the test and was aware that on a previous occasion when the gyros had been covered the machine had continued to lift. At my request he now wrote me a paper on this particular issue in the light of the positive outcome of the laboratory test.

He said it was 'most unlikely' that my machine was producing vertical thrust in a similar way to a helicopter, then went on to explain:

> The principle of helicopter theory in normal flight is that a change of momentum of air in the vertical direction is induced by the rotor, which in turn is manifested by a pressure difference on the rotor blades. The momentum change is the product of mass of air times the velocity change and unless the closed box was very leaky this will be small. There is an additional effect known as 'ground effect'. When a helicopter is close to the ground the down-flowing air has difficulty in escaping below the rotor and generates a static pressure rise which increases the lift. Hovercraft take this to an extreme and most of their lift comes from this feature, but again you need a lot of air to get much lift and any reasonable test should have detected whether there was a lot of breeze in the test cell. If the test apparatus was suspended some distance from any floor or table which might produce ground effect, then such a consideration can probably be dismissed. There is an additional effect which must be dismissed which one might call the hot air balloon effect (buoyancy). This would come about if the internals of the box warm up and the box leaks very slightly so as to vent some of the internal air to atmosphere, the weight of the air inside the box thus being reduced. Knowledge of the internal temperature and pressure during the test, and the size of the box, would lead to a simple calculation of the quantity of lift possible. This effect I would have thought to be more likely to be present in the Melbourne test than the helicopter effect.

There could now be no further speculation on this matter. The fact that my machine had been in a sealed compartment within its container meant there could have been no displacement of free-flowing air or down draught to make it function like a helicopter. There was also no warm air in the compartment because the engine unit had been housed separately in the lower, open section of the box. But, in any case, all these factors were far too obvious not to have been eliminated by the laboratory team in the first place.

Rupert Lucas summed up his paper by describing the question often put to engineers at a job interview. They are told that a farmer has a trailer full of birds. Because he is worried by the weight on the wheels of the trailer, plus the weight of the birds, he keeps stirring the birds up so they are constantly flying about inside the trailer. Question: Has he reduced the load on the wheels? Answer: It depends. If the trailer is totally enclosed with a solid material there is no change of momentum of the system as a whole because the lift experienced by the birds is being exactly countered by pressure on the floor. This duly accords with Newton's Third Law that every force applied creates an equal and opposite reaction and in this case means the trailer's weight remains the same. If, however, the trailer is only covered in with chicken wire, allowing the free passage of air, then the birds when in flight are no longer part of the system and the weight on the wheels will be reduced accordingly.

In other words, if my machine in a sealed environment lost weight, as it had done, then logically, in my view, this must have been because it was producing a non-Newtonian force.

The existence of a laboratory report caused other interesting reactions. A group of mathematicians at an English university said they 'dearly' wanted to investigate what appeared to be a new, natural phenomenon. The letter assured me: 'There is no question of the scientific community ridiculing your work. Instead there is great curiosity.' At the same time one of the science journals offered to buy the exclusive rights to the full report. All such requests, however, were firmly rejected. I was determined to resist all temptations to release further information until authorized by BWN.

I faced my stiffest challenge on this score shortly afterwards when the BBC, in response to viewers' requests, featured my work on their top science programme 'Tomorrow's World'. They showed a clip of the original Grampian documentary and displayed my first machine in a static state in the studio. After describing what my device was claimed to have done both inside and outside the laboratory, the presenter conducted a number of demonstrations with gyroscopes to show their behaviour under rotation. Then he carried out an experiment with a small gyroscope in an attempt to prove that reactionless thrust was nothing more than an illusion. The gyroscope was weighed on a set of scales while spinning and again when at rest. The weight on both occasions remained the same and so the presenter loftily declared that an anti-gravity machine must be regarded with a great deal of scepticism until the full laboratory report was published. The superficial nature of the demonstration and the conclusion drawn from it left me flabbergasted and angry. On the other hand, I had suspected that such a cynical treatment would be given to the story. But by throwing down the gauntlet before an audience of ten million viewers to publish the full report, the BBC had placed me in a very difficult position. When the local Press reported the following morning what had unfolded during the programme, I felt forced to issue a statement pointing out that independent experts had already examined the laboratory report and none of them had rejected it. I also said that in view of the mounting pressure I would ask the Australian company once more if they would release the full report. The headline in the evening newspaper that day announced: 'Sandy Hoping to Shock the Cynics'. I sent off a fax to Noel Carroll explaining my predicament and pointing out that the integrity of my machine had been put on the line. But the millionaire on the other side of the world remained unmoved.

However, this latest wave of public interest in anti-gravity machines had brought forward an exciting proposal from Professor Stephen Salter at Edinburgh University, with the backing of the Advanced Energy Research Institute in London. Both, of course, had been monitoring events very carefully since my machine had first appeared on the scene eighteen months before. Now a sponsor had been found who was interested in backing a public examination of all known gyro thrust machines in a determined and dramatic effort to establish once and for all whether such devices were indeed capable of creating a force contrary to the laws of physics. It was intended to hold this unique scientific meeting at Edinburgh University where the testing procedure would be supervised by a panel of experts under the watchful gaze of the media. The professor lost no time in preparing a detailed prospectus for the 'anti-gravity' convention and sent if off to all the people he knew to have a gyroscopic device. In the introduction he said:

At least a dozen inventors have claimed that gyros can be used to produce a sustained undirectional thrust without any reaction. This would apparently contradict Newton's Third Law of Motion. The scientific implications of a convincing proof of the claim are profound. Furthermore one of the limitations to deep space flight would be removed if the consumption of mass in a rocket exhaust could be eliminated. Discussions of the claims must involve a comparison of two probabilities. Probability A is that nearly all the physicists who ever lived have got a piece of basic physics badly wrong. Probability B is that a much smaller number of people have got in a muddle about a laboratory experiment. Anyone who has ever done anything in a laboratory will admit that probability B is higher than probability A.

But the history of science shows clearly that probability A is not absolutely zero. Indeed, many of the most notable scientific advances have followed the careful investigation of some annoying inconsistency. This note describes the apparatus to test the claims. The objective is that, after an agreed set of trials, either the most sceptical conventionalist should be convinced that the claims are true or that the most enthusiastic of the inventors should be convinced that they are false. This difficult objective may be achieved more easily if inventors and scrutineers have the opportunity to study this document carefully, add extra features to the design, and then lodge a formal statement as to which experimental results would convince them that their previous opinions were incorrect.

Salter proposed that a test bed be built which could accommodate all the machines on a common basis and be of a design simple enough to minimize disputes over its operation and, in the long term, provide an apparatus acceptable as the standard test for such devices. He wanted a test bed strong enough to take the weight of both the machine and its inventor, one that would support the heaviest device but still be able to sense the output of the lightest. To that end he envisaged the construction of two large rectangular steel frames. The bigger of the two would be bolted to a concrete floor, the other frame, with a wooden deck to accommodate both inventor and machine, would be hung inside it in such a way that it would move forward under the influence of a thrusting force. This movement would be measured by a battery of electronic equipment.

The prospectus went to great lengths to devise a procedure which would be seen to be scrupulously fair, accurate and acceptable to all those taking part in what the tabloids would inevitably have described as a 'Flying Saucer Convention'. There was even an invitation to the scrutineers to: 'Climb on to the platform and jump, dance, swing weights, wrestle, etc, without producing any net thrust. Only by throwing objects off the platform, or by employing aerodynamic methods, should they be able to induce any net thrust. The scrutineers should be encouraged to devise a variety of such tests to convince themselves of the soundness of the test bed design. They should then lodge a written declaration of their confidence in the test method together with any caveats. They should calculate a minimum figure for the net force which they would accept as a positive result . . . '

Whether I could have taken part in such a convention as this was highly doubtful. If BWN wouldn't allow publication of the laboratory report, I simply couldn't see them giving me the go-ahead to display the machine itself in public where it could be examined by outsiders at close quarters. In the event such a decision never had to be taken. The response to the prospectus was so lukewarm, with most inventors not even bothering to reply, that the whole idea had to be dropped. The organizers and the sponsoring company were disappointed that such a promising opportunity to test the truth of established physics had been lost. Perhaps the prospect of having their machines so ruthlessly exposed to public examination was too much for most of the inventors. The fear of failure and the risk of ridicule may have been too great for people who cherished their brainchilds and believed them to be genuine and beyond suspicion. But I know that if the climate were to change such a convention could still be staged at some future time. The organizers have not written it off.

No sooner had the furore over the latest news of my machine calmed down again in Britain than the whole business flared up once more, this time in Australia. Until now Ron Thompson had resisted launching the story as a separate entity down under, preferring the news to filter through from our own media at home. This he felt would reduce any undue harassment for BWN and myself while I was working in Dandenong. But it was only a matter of time before the Australian media were demanding to get in on the act as well. Towards the end of 1988 I was contacted by the London-based reporter of the Australian Broadcasting Corporation who wanted to record a piece with myself and Professor Salter for their national radio programme,

'The Science Show'. Shortly afterwards a Sydney-based television production company, whose regular science programme 'Beyond 2000' is syndicated to sixty countries round the world, asked if they could send a film unit to Dundee to cover my story. At the same time Thompson was asked to write a feature article for the mass circulation magazine *Good Weekend*. By now there seemed no point in dodging these requests and so we went ahead on all fronts of the Australian media with the same self-imposed restrictions as before, except for BWN's anonymity. We decided to identify the company for the first time, believing it was no longer practical to conceal the name in view of the extensive coverage about to be given within the home country.

From the now predictable stream of letters and phone calls arising from these stories there emerged one very interesting proposition. It came first by telephone and then by letter from Errol White, who runs his own company in Sydney importing and manufacturing light curable products. His main interest outside his own business was the design of airships. For fifteen years he had been trying to find a way of transforming these balloon vehicles into a form capable of replacing the car as the normal means of family transport. A country like Australia with its vast open spaces was especially amenable to this type of travel.

Airships are kept aloft by balloons full of gas and use aerodynamics in the shape of ailerons and rudder to alter direction and altitude. Their movements are slow and cumbersome. They are powered by internal combustion engines linked to propellers. Errol White, like many people, realized that this mixture of aeroplane and floating balloon could never be adapted to the domestic market. What was required, he said, was a revolutionary propulsion unit to give instant manoeuvrability to smaller airships which could then be parked alongside houses in the same way as the family saloon. He regarded my anti-gravity machine as having that potential. I, of course, had always been aware of the possibility of the flying motor car using a gyroscopic invention such as mine. But I hadn't actually envisaged it in quite this way. Errol assured me that if my machine could provide the required thrust he could draw on millions of dollars of funding to usher in an exciting new generation of airships. 'As soon as you can give me lift factors and physical sizes we will swing into action with the design work,' he wrote. 'The big money people I have lined up for such a venture are ready and eager to go.'

Prospects for my pioneering work had never seemed so bright. The level of public interest was gathering momentum all the time. But, unknown to me then, there were other, even bigger fish already swimming towards my shore.

Chapter 18

It was a fine, early winter's afternoon in Scotland, several weeks after my return from the latest laboratory tests in Melbourne, when Janet and I decided to go for a country ramble. Our house on the outskirts of Dundee is only twenty miles from the rugged glen of Angus, a world of rustic beauty far removed from the clatter of engineering workshops and the devilish complexities of gyroscopic machines. For several hours until dusk we roamed through woods and over heather-clad slopes with our two Yorkshire terriers, oblivious to all the pressures of life in the solitude and grandeur of our temporary haven.

When we arrived back home at six the phone was ringing as I swung open the front door. It was Ron Thompson on the line and I could tell from his clipped tones that he was pretty excited about something. He wanted to come round right away. Ten minutes later he was sitting in the lounge unfolding the events of that afternoon while we had been out on the hills. Returning to the office from a filming assignment, he had found a note on his desk asking him to return a call to a Mr Evans at a number prefixed by a code he couldn't recognize. He assumed it was simply another of the many enquiries he was now in the habit of receiving from members of the public anxious to know a bit more about my machine. But when he phoned back he thought he was hearing things when a switchboard operator announced the name of British Aerospace. He was through to their military aircraft division at Warton Aerodrome near Preston in Lancashire. This is one of Europe's most advanced research and development centres for combat aircraft projects of the future. Mr Evans turned out to be Dr Ronald Evans, Principal Engineer of Future Concepts.

He told Thompson he had a special, personal interest in gyroscopes and had been following my progress very closely through all the media coverage. British Aerospace had also purchased a video copy of the original television documentary 'The Man Who Wants to Change the World'. Having read about the successful outcome of the laboratory tests he felt the time had now arrived when he would like to meet me personally and, insofar as I was able to, discuss my work. Like Thompson, I was intrigued and not a little flattered by this unexpected interest at such an exalted level.

I had, of course, to be careful to whom I spoke and what I said in view of my obvious obligation to BWN. But this didn't mean I had to become a shadowy, reclusive figure unable to open my mouth. I could see nothing wrong with a frank exchange of views on the subject of anti-gravity technology. In any case, as far as my own original machine was concerned the patent application had now been published and was available to the public. When Dr Evans contacted me to make an appointment he made it clear that although his bosses at British Aerospace knew about this approach he would be coming to see me in a purely prrrivate capacity. I understood the situation immediately. It was the same arrangement as during the war when British agents were parachuted behind enemy lines. If they were successful and eluded capture they became heroes. If they failed and were picked up no one wanted to know them. Dr Evans duly arrived at my house incognito. He had slipped into Dundee by car when no one was looking.

He was a likeable man, softly spoken and of gentle demeanour. He had the air of a boffin and had brought with him a number of set-piece demonstrations which he proceeded to run through in my lounge. He fired up a small gyro in a gimbal and by holding it in his fingers made it twist violently as it reacted sharply to sudden changes in the position of his hand. We then watched a large cardboard wheel spinning at the end of a string in different planes of rotation. Later he displayed the aerodynamic properties of a cardboard boomerang as it soared round the room dodging in and out of the furniture. All this was simply a bit of light-hearted groundwork to break the ice and lead us into the serious business of discussing what I had observed and achieved so far by using gyroscopes as a form of propulsion.

It soon emerged that Dr Evans, an applied mathematician, was interested in the possible existence of what had become known as the Fifth Force of nature. The four forces already well established are gravity, electromagnetism, and two others contained within atoms. The elusive Fifth Force is believed by many academics to act as a counter to gravity and to be the result of attraction between large masses over intermediate distances. The search to confirm the presence of this new element in physics has been going on for some ten years since experiments in a deep Australian mine suggested that there might be another force at work. Evans said that if such a force did exist it could be the medium on which inertial drive machines reacted and if this was so, he concluded, Newton's Laws of Motion would remain intact.

This, of course, was not the first time that the phenomenon of my machine had been linked to the presence of other natural forces, as yet untapped, in the atmosphere. Such speculation had been a continuing theme throughout the years of discussion over my invention. As I've mentioned earlier, the famous physicist Oliver Heaviside was predicting such an energy source at the turn of the century.

By the time he left early that evening I knew without doubt that my visitor from British Aerospace was a man with an open mind, as one would expect in someone who shared responsibility for shaping our aeronautical future. He seemed satisfied with everything I told him about my machine. He read the laboratory report. Then he asked me if I would be willing to visit his establishment at Warton and have further talks with some of the company's other senior men. I said I would, realizing that if such a meeting were to take place, everything would move on to a much more official basis than his private visit that afternoon. The invitation arrived only two days later. A week after that Janet and I were motoring down the M6 for our rendezvous with the top brass.

The military aircraft division at Warton is obviously a high security operation where all visitors are carefully vetted and signed in by people of certain authority. Ron Evans was there to guide us through the system and before long we found ourselves in a conference room where half a dozen engineers and physicists were waiting to greet us. With only a break for lunch, we spent most of the day discussing the potential of inertial thrust machines, studying the laboratory report on my device, and analysing the video of the Grampian documentary. Everyone seemed impressed with what I had achieved so far but inevitably they wanted to know if they could see one of my machines in action and, if possible, tested in their own laboratory. Confidentiality would be guaranteed. I now found myself in a very tricky position. My first reaction was to refuse the request because of my commitment to the Australians. On the other hand, I was anxious to continue this dialogue with experts who were working at the highest level in the national interest and at the same time wanted to follow up my theories. I had to find a formula for my own conscience which would allow me to demonstrate my apparatus to British Aerospace while not being seen as going behind the back of BWN.

I finally overcame the quandary by agreeing to show them a new machine altogether, one I had been building with my own resources and in my own time since returning home from my last trip. My two laboratory-tested devices were still in Australia and would eventually be shipped out to California for the next stage of the development programme. But I had now been told by BWN that because of various other pressures within the company my departure date for Pasadena was being put back several months. Rather than sit and twiddle my fingers, I had started to put together another machine with conventional gyros to try and iron out for myself the various problems I had encountered with my ball device. It was this latest, untried machine that I would take to British Aerospace. It would not incorporate the design features of the ball machine, but simply conform to the specification already protected under the patent application for my first Australian device. I could see no harm in proceeding along these lines. Indeed, there was no saying what spin-offs there could be for BWN as a result of this exercise.

My new machine – prototype Mark Seven – was ready by the third week of January 1989, and Ron Evans made the necessary arrangements to have it tested in one of the laboratories at Warton. Janet and I set off once more for the Lancashire coast, this time with the new machine safely packed away in the boot of the car. We had been booked into the same hotel in St Anne's as on our previous visit. We simply told our friends we were off again for a few days by the sea. Being the middle of winter some of them thought we were crackers but the weather was rather mild so it didn't seem too outlandish a reason to give for our absence from home at that time of year.

We spent two full days in the laboratory where the test procedure was much the same as in Melbourne, with the machine inside a box hanging by cord from an overhead beam fitted with strain gauges. The first day was mostly occupied by calibrating the equipment and making sure that everything was shipshape for the trials. There was time left, however, for a couple of quick runs, but these yielded no lift so I fitted smaller gyros for the following day. The next morning we had no sooner started running the device in earnest when we encountered problems with the radio control system for the machine's engine. This was traced to run-down batteries in the receiver. British Aerospace could give me almost anything I wanted from their engineering workshops and laboratories at Warton but ironically they didn't have the small batteries which were vital to the whole operation. There then followed a frantic hunt through Blackpool, a few miles away, to find a shop that could supply the necessary. By the time we tracked down the batteries it was well into Friday afternoon and, with the weekend coming up, it was agreed we should return at a later date to give the machine a proper chance to prove itself.

Two weeks later Janet and I were back behind the tall fences at Warton. But the laboratory results were disappointing. Only two of the runs gave a positive reading and on each occasion the measurement was only a fraction of an ounce. This was not enough, said Ron Evans, to justify British Aerospace taking any further interest at that stage. He emphasized, however, that their door was open to me at any time if I felt I had something new to show them in the future.

Strangely enough, my lack of success at one of the country's top engineering establishments didn't worry me although, naturally, I was a bit upset, knowing perfectly well that my work could produce far better results. I had built a machine closely resembling the first device which had sailed through the laboratory tests in Melbourne, but I realized I must have unwittingly introduced a different feature into its design. Hard experience had taught me that it took very little to upset the balance of forces contained within a gyroscopic propulsion unit. It didn't take me long to discover that on this occasion the difference lay in the kind of rubber belts I had used in the drive system to the gyros and the machine. I had switched to a type with less elasticity and this had reduced the machine's ability to accommodate fluctuations in speed. I then went on to discover that the most critical factor of all in achieving lift lay in the drive mechanism. It had to give the system a measure of flexibility to react to the changing speeds of rotation. After many months of trial and error I finally built a special transmission system that would apply the power in the most effective way. Although my ball machine was still in Australia and couldn't immediately be fitted with this new drive system, I was certain that it would transform the performance of that troublesome device. It was certainly working wonders with the British Aerospace machine which was now going great guns in my garage, consistently producing a generous measure of vertical thrust against the counterweight.

171

Although this new area of investigation into my work gave me plenty to occupy myself with, I was starting to get slightly concerned about the future intentions of BWN. By the middle of February 1989, I had been at home for four months and apart from being told my move to California had been postponed there had been little contact with the Australian company. I realized that Noel Carroll was involved in many other projects apart from mine, but there is something slightly disconcerting about your salary popping up in the bank every month while never hearing from your benefactor. Then, suddenly, at five in the morning I was wakened by a call from Dandenong. It was Noel Carroll's secretary telling me the boss was coming to London the following week and wanted to see me at the Waldorf Hotel where he would be staying for several days while attending to other business. I breathed a sigh of relief. Surely now things would start moving again and we could implement our plan to press ahead on a team basis as previously agreed?

On the day of our meeting Janet and I caught an early shuttle from Edinburgh to Heathrow and then, unlike most people bound for the Waldorf, completed the journey to our posh destination by tube. When we reached the hotel I reported to reception. A minute later we were being whisked up by lift to Mr Carroll's suite. Noel, flanked by two of his executives, welcomed us like long lost friends. Over the next few hours we discussed once more the future of the Kidd Machine, with my millionaire backer appearing to have lost none of his enthusiasm for the project. But although Pasadena kept cropping up in the conversation, it was obvious that Noel's own preference of location had swung back to Australia where BWN were in the final stages of building a new factory complex with laboratory facilities near the existing plant at Dandenong. As a first step, however, he now wanted all the academic groundwork on my ball machine carried out in Britain. This would involve a large part of the programme previously earmarked for Pasadena: a test rig to work through all the variables in sizes, weights and angles to find the most effective specification for producing maximum lift and a mathematical formula to provide the basis for future development.

The natural person to undertake such an assignment was Professor Eric Laithwaite, the man whose television lecture on gyroscopes had originally inspired me, and to whom I had first turned with my original machine. Indeed, in the endorsement he had given me at that time, four years before, he had stated his willingness to act as consultant on future development work. Although we hadn't spoken much since then he had been constantly quoted in the newspaper coverage of my machine's progress and had been one of the panel who had studied the laboratory report. Noel agreed that I should approach him now and offer him the contract.

Several days later I returned to London and met the professor by arrangement at Imperial College where he had been granted a 'grace and favour' office on his official retirement three years earlier. We discussed the machine and all its ramifications for over two hours. But sadly we couldn't see eye to eye on the way the device was producing its vertical lift. He simply wasn't prepared to accept my theory on the state of change the gyros were going through to create their force. It was a real cut and thrust session in which both of us refused to budge. Academically, it was a David and Goliath situation. Here was I, a graduate from a garden shed, pitching against an intellectual giant on his home ground at Imperial College. But, as I've made plain before, professorships, doctorates and degrees have never overawed me and, to be fair, Eric Laithwaite had never sought to patronize me on that score. He had always treated me as an equal. On this occasion, however, I held the trump hand. I was the inventor and I knew my machine better than anyone else. Sometimes I thought I knew it even better than myself! Finally, unable to reconcile our views, the professor said he could not enter into the project. I was sorry that our meeting had ended in this way. Teaming up with the professor would have been a fairytale touch in the circumstances. But it was not to be.

At that time, of course, I was aware he was facing problems of his own with experimental work in the field of alternative energy. British financiers had chipped in £70,000 for a machine he had built to demonstrate the feasibility of a gyroscopic device tapping inertial radiation in space. But UK funding had dried up and he now had no accommodation in which to run his bulky, prototype machine. It was lying in boxes at Imperial College. His work had come to a standstill.

All this had been fully reported in *The Times* along with a statement from the professor in which he had revived the theme of the brain drain. He was quoted: 'Prince Charles hit the nail on the head when he said other countries are exploiting our developments. It is very frustrating to see Japan, Germany and America developing our ideas such as high-speed transport systems. There is never anyone prepared to put enough money into inventions in this country. British firms always want the profit guaranteed by the end of the year or they will not support.' The article had then gone on to explain how Laithwaite had suffered before in this way when his development of the linear electric motor had been virtually ignored in Britain while exploited abroad, with the shuttle train from Birmingham International Airport believed to be the only example of linear motor propulsion for trains working in Britain.

Not for the first time I realized how fortunate I had been, particularly as a non-academic, in finding a wealthy backer for my machine. Perhaps the professor was conscious of this too. I could certainly understand his frustration and it was with a real sense of regret that I walked out of Imperial College that day knowing we had come to the parting of the ways.

On the flight back to Scotland I racked my brains over who I should turn to now. It made sense to involve someone who was familiar with my work. There was no way I was going to hawk my machine round until I found an academic who was on my side and prepared to get involved in such a controversial project. Professor Salter, I knew, was heavily committed on other projects at Edinburgh University. But there was still Allan Barr, head of the engineering department at Aberdeen University. He had studied my laboratory report and although restrained in his optimism had felt that my machine was certainly worthy of further examination. I went to see him at the university and he agreed to look at my latest device with a view to accepting a consultancy.

By now I had adopted a much more effective rig in my garage. Instead of having the machine tethered to the workbench, giving it restricted movement against the counterweight system, the device was now housed inside an aluminium cage and suspended from an overhead rafter by cord, at the other end of which was attached the counterbalance. This resembled the setup in the laboratory except, of course, I had no sophisticated measuring instruments with which to accurately calculate the thrust. I still had to depend on the lump of cast iron with magnet and small spanners. But at least the machine was no longer in contact with a solid surface and was now visually much more impressive when it rose up, climbing slowly into the roof of the garage under the power of its inertial thrust.

Professor Barr saw this happen for himself several weeks later. It was the first time he had seen one of my machines in action and he stayed in the garage for a considerable time watching the device go through a series of successful runs. Finally he said he would be willing to carry out an analysis of the machine's behaviour with a

174

view to working out the maths involved. This, of course, would be subject to the negotiation of a contract between BWN and the university. I was delighted with his decision. It was now up to me to make certain that my latest machine would give of its best when I handed it over to the experts at Aberdeen University. I certainly couldn't afford a repeat of the anti-climax at British Aerospace. I was, however, completely confident that with all the recent improvements in the drive mechanism I would get even better results than achieved in the first laboratory trials in Melbourne. Anything less would be a big disappointment. I was hungry for a bit more success, particularly in view of the problems I had experienced over the ball machine. The omens were good. Although garage tests were far from being perfect, I could tell from the manner in which my machine was now climbing away from the counterweight that it was in fine fettle.

Yes, it was good to know that after a lengthy spell of uncertainty the Kidd Machine looked as if it was about to take to the road again. For the past five months I had undergone another period of incarceration in my shed and garage, trying to fathom out ways of improving my device while the Australians made up their minds what to do next. Janet had kept telling me I was back to where I had started. In a way, of course, she was right. I thought my shed days were over when I walked into Dundee University. I was absolutely certain I had seen the last of them when I had taken off for Australia. But here I was, back in the old prison cell, working my old tools, with hardly enough room in which to turn. In that sense, I suppose, I had gone into reverse. On the other hand, this was where it had all taken shape in the first place. This was the cradle of my very first machine. I felt at home here in my familiar surroundings. The smell of creosoted wood in my shed and the constant buzz of conversation from people passing in the lane just outside my garage, not to mention our two Yorkies constantly under my feet, were all comforting reminders of that part of the world I loved best of all. In fact, it had struck me many times during these past months that nothing I had done in Australia couldn't have been accomplished equally well in my own backyard. I had still only been a one-man band in the BWN factory at Dandenong. Even the laboratory tests could have been carried out in Scotland. It was really ironic to think that I had been removed from a country steeped in engineering tradition and plonked down in the middle of another one 12,000 miles away where the facilities were certainly no better than I could get at home.

I don't, however, wish to give the impression that I was ungrateful to Noel Carroll. It was he, after all, who had picked up the pieces after I had been 'sent down' from Dundee University. It was his financial backing that was allowing me to eat and look after my family while continuing to work flat out on my machine. He had gone along patiently with all my theories. I had much to thank him for. The experience down under had given Janet and me the opportunity of travelling and meeting other people. It was inevitable that we would be back in Australia again. But the question that has to be asked is simply this: Is it a wise thing to uproot an inventor from his natural environment, transplant him into a totally different culture far from home, and then expect him to carry on producing his best work? I am sure that is not always the recipe for success. Particularly if, like me, you are a real homebird who likes to be surrounded by his loved ones.

You may think all this is irrelevant. But to get the engineering right you must also try to get the psychology right too. I would respectfully recommend to all venture capitalists that, provided their protégés can be trusted to keep their shoulder to the wheel, they should allow them to carry on their work as long as possible in their natural habitat.

Chapter 19

Noel Carroll had a bee in his bonnet about putting one of my machines through an underwater test to supplement the results already obtained in the Melbourne laboratory. He had mentioned this possibility on several occasions during my last spell in Australia. Finally, in the summer of 1989, in one of the regular phone calls he now made to me since our 'summit' at the Waldorf Hotel, he asked me to go ahead and prepare a device which would be suitable for such an appraisal. At the time I was waiting on the Aberdeen University project being confirmed.

I fully understood why he was so keen to have this done. A laboratory report is all very nice but it has to be studied, understood, interpreted, and then, of course, accepted before it proves anything. People can pick holes in it, questioning the accuracy of the testing equipment or raising the spectre of human error. These doubts had already been expressed. There is another drawback about statistical reports. They don't exactly set the heather on fire for the average person who sees the phenomenon of inertial thrust in terms of a flying saucer. A machine which has been deemed to have done something by calculation, 'invisibly' as it were like mine in the laboratory, lacks a certain glamour.

The way round this is to provide first-hand, visual evidence instead. Experts can huff and puff all they want over facts and figures in a report. But if you can actually let them see something happen before their very eyes they must either accept that experience or arrange to see an oculist. This is what Noel wanted: a machine which could be instantly seen to do the 'impossible'. The water test was certainly one way of achieving that. A device able to move itself through water without propellers sinks Newton's Third Law without trace. But when he gave me my starting orders my groans must have been heard all the way to Australia. It wasn't the adaptation of a machine for such a test that concerned me, but all the other problems associated with going underwater.

The test would involve putting the machine into a sealed metal container and submerging it to a certain depth in the tank by the use of flood chambers. This is called neutral buoyancy and involves the same principle as the submarine. You must make certain the container is always properly sealed against seepage and you also have to stabilize it. Remember, there is now a machine thrashing about inside that hull causing a lot of movement.

The power to drive the device and the gyros would be another headache. This would have to be supplied by electric motors with batteries which would require constant recharging. Apart from all these drawbacks the water test is fine. It is just a pain in the backside to set up.

For several weeks I did nothing but contemplate the prospect of going through all this hassle, making no move in the hope that somehow the water test would miraculously disappear. Just when it seemed there was no escape an envelope arrived from Australia. It contained a note from one of BWN's senior engineers enclosing a magazine article he thought I would find interesting. It had been written by a prominent American engineer and author called Harry Stine and was the inside story of the famous space machine called the Dean Machine or the Dean Drive about which I had already heard.

But what I had not known about until reading Stine's article in *Analog Science Fiction/Science Fact* was the existence of a special test which had been devised to establish the truth of Dean's highly controversial invention. A diagram showing how that test was carried out appeared on one of the pages. I gazed at the drawing for several seconds. Then, suddenly, it clicked. There, before my very eyes, was the answer. It was the simplest, yet most effective, visual test for an anti-gravity machine you could ever think of. There was no need for water tanks or laboratories. No need for measuring equipment. This test could be carried out anywhere at anytime with not much more than a ball of string. It was a test which had been suggested to me before but one I had dismissed at the time as being impractical for my machine.

That had been in 1986 when Ron Thompson had spoken to another American engineer and science writer, Jerry Pournelle, to tell him about my original machine. Pournelle had said that one sure way of finding out if the device was genuine was to hang it from a piece of string fixed to the ceiling. If the machine could displace itself from the vertical and move just a tiny distance sideways under the power of its gyros, and stay in that position, then there could be absolutely no doubt. The laws of physics, he said, would simply have to be changed. This, of course, was a horizontal test and not the vertical one for which all my machines had been designed. Nevertheless, all I thought I had to do was to make one or two minor adjustments and then turn the device on its side. What baffled me at the time was how my device, rotating at the end of a cord with spinning gyros, could be held steady long enough to establish if it was moving horizontally under its own steam. It seemed inevitable to me that a machine producing all this frantic motion would be bound to swivel and swing all over the place.

I thought nothing more about this test until coming across the rig described by Pournelle in Harry Stine's article. But there was one critical difference. Instead of the single cord I assumed the device would hang from there were actually two, each one fixed to a different part of the machine's housing to give it the vital stability I had been looking for. The whole thing was so simple I almost kicked myself. Why this solution had never struck me before I'll never understand.

In the article Stine describes how, as a young assistant director of research with a corporation in Connecticut interested in developing new industrial products, he and his boss set out one morning in September 1960 to drive to Washington DC. They had an appointment with a civil service employee by the name of Norman Dean who lived in an apartment on Wisconsin Avenue. They had been tipped off that Dean had invented a sensational anti-gravity machine which could produce a thrust equal to eighty-five pounds.

It was an entirely different concept to mine. Instead of gyroscopes, it was based on two electrically-driven, counter-rotating flywheels which had a force applied to them at a certain part of each cycle. This caused the whole machine, weighing one hundred and thirty-five pounds, to move across the floor on ball-bearing wheels. Stine explained how he and his director, Dr William O. Davis, a former head of scientific research in the American Airforce, had witnessed the Dean Drive do precisely that in one of the rooms of the apartment. He then gave this extract from a joint report they had made on that visit:

> The device he showed us did not levitate, but applied a lateral force to a mass. Both of us approached this unlikely device with scepticism. The mechanism was constructed of metal and lucite

in such a way that the moving parts were clearly visible. We checked for the usual gimmicks of air hoses and the like but found nothing. The model rested on the waxed floor of Dean's apartment on the eighth floor of a modern apartment house. Hidden magnets seemed unlikely and in any event could not account for the magnitude of the forces displayed, particularly since there appeared to be very little ferritic material in the device. The drive was arranged so as to apply its output to a push-rod which was fastened to a reaction mass (also open) which appeared to weigh approximately three times as much as the drive unit. We inspected both the drive and the reaction mass before and after the demonstration and are convinced that both were free to move on the polished surface of the floor. There was no observable tilt to the floor. Both masses rested on flange-type feet and no scratches were observed on the floor when either was slid. When the drive was brought up to speed and the clutch mechanism activated, the drive was observed to produce a force such that the reaction mass was moved several millimeters in a gradual, steady manner while the drive unit did not move at all when observed closely with the naked eye from a distance of only a few inches. A second experiment was performed where the reaction mass was replaced by each of our hands in turn. When the drive operated, a definite force was felt which increased with pressure and produced motion of the hand against the pressure. With the drive turned off the same pressure easily moved the drive unit several inches. It was the conclusion of us both that we had witnessed a real anomaly and that the possibility of fraud in the demonstration was slim. When this is combined with the testimony of other competent witnesses, some of whom have witnessed the weight-reduction experiment, it seems increasingly likely that Dean has produced a genuine new phenomenon.

Stine described Dean as a 'typical amateur tinkerer and inventor' with no formal training as an engineer or scientist and therefore blissfully unaware that, theoretically, his machine could never succeed. Stine and Davis, recognizing the huge potential of the Dean Drive, excitedly got to work on investigating the principles of what they saw as a future space system. The trouble was they had no success in dealing with Mr Dean. 'Most inventors want a million dollars and Dean was hardly an exception to the rule,' wrote Stine.

Unable, therefore, to get their hands on Dean's invention, which was covered by patent anyway, they built an experimental device based on a new concept of mechanics created by Davis to accommodate the critical elements of the revolutionary machine. The research programme went on for five long years and only ended, inconclusively, when the company ran into hard times and everyone on the project was paid off. According to Stine nothing had been resolved over the Dean Drive. Basically it remained a mystery. In 1962, William Davis published his new physics theory as 'The Fourth Law of Motion' which was regarded by the scientific fraternity as interesting but not terribly valuable. Norman Dean himself died in the late 1960s and it seems his machine was never seen again. But the one thing that did survive was the rig which had been devised to test the experimental apparatus. They called it the 'critical pendulum test' and that was the one which now held my attention. Harry Stine saw it as the ultimate 'truth' test for all space drives and anti-gravity machines. He wrote:

When word got out that the Huyck Research Center would listen to inventors and look at their machines, the fun began. I think that I have seen every sort of shaking, spinning, whirling, vibrating, buzzing, snarling, grinding space drive that the fertile imagination of inventors can dream up. I have seen ones that would climb a slight gradient because of the stick-slip frictional phenomenon. I've seen them scoot across the floor. I have seen them do all sorts of wonderful things *except* when we put them to the critical pendulum test . . . Every space drive that we tested would not pass the test. The inventors were usually very embarrassed. 'Gee, it just started to work there when it came apart. I guess we're lucky that nobody was hurt when it blew up.' They all left promising to fix the invention and return with it. Nobody ever did. There is one highly unfortunate aspect to this. Because of the total recalcitrance of Norman L. Dean we were never able to subject the Dean Drive itself to the critical pendulum test.'

Today Harry Stine, now sixty-one, lives in Phoenix, Arizona. He has written more than forty books on scientific subjects and has served as a science correspondent for both television and radio. He is also a consultant in astronautical history to the National Air and Space Museum at the Smithsonian Institute in Washington. In his entry in

Who's Who in America he is quoted: 'I grew up on a vanishing frontier and intend to spend my life opening new frontiers – in space, because the world is no more closed than it is flat. Because of this we do not live in a world of limits, but a limitless universe, and have a limitless future.' That certainly makes him my kind of man.

Before starting to prepare my own machine for the pendulum test I wanted to check out certain aspects of the rig to make absolutely sure I would be sticking rigidly to the rules. Suspecting that Harry Stine had possibly dealt with enough inventors in his time, I got Ron Thompson to make the phone call. He found Stine extremely affable and only too pleased to give him clarification on all the points he raised. He said he had heard of the Kidd Machine. He also told Ron that although his article had been published ten years previously the test had continued to defy every machine that had come its way since. 'If Mr Kidd's device comes through my test it will be the first in the world to do so as far as I'm aware,' he said. 'If that were to happen the consequences would be shattering.'

I wasted no time in rigging up the test. Although hanging the cords from the roof of the garage was a simple enough task, there were two important requirements. Each cord had to be anchored in two places about six inches apart so that each one came down to form a 'V' at the point it was attached to the machine. This would give the device maximum stability. The cords also had to drop a reasonable distance from the roof. The longer they were the more sensitive their reaction would be to the movement of the machine. Even a small thrust would cause a visible deflection on long cords. However, I was restricted in my garage to a six-foot drop, allowing the machine to hang twelve inches off the floor.

With my latest machine, the air-cooled engine, drive mechanism and fuel tank were all positioned on the roof of the aluminium cage housing the device. Apart from turning the fuel tank round to avoid spillage, there was little else to do except turn the whole unit on its side. The machine, of course, had never been designed to lie in a horizontal position and because of this I realized that the gravitational forces upon the gyros would now be quite different. In the vertical mode both gyros were having to overcome the same downward pull as they rose upwards. But now, with the machine on its side, gravity would be affecting the gyros in opposite ways. During each revolution of the machine the bottom gyro would continue to rise against gravity whereas the top one, also moving inwards, would be pulled down by that very same force. This would have a significant effect on the performance of the machine. Effectively, it would now only be able to utilize the thrust of one gyro instead of two. But despite this, I was certain the device would still have the energy to displace itself from the vertical and move forwards in mid-air.

What I hadn't bargained for, however, was the way in which the top gyro would collapse so completely. During the first run, before the machine had a chance to do anything, it simply toppled inwards, clattering against the main shaft and damaging various parts of the mechanism. I had never expected the reaction to be so drastic. After repairing the fairly extensive damage, I had to think of a way of preventing the gyros falling below a certain point when in the upper position. Finally I fitted restraining links to the gyro arms. Then I started my second set of horizontal trials.

As I gradually built up the speed of the gyros with my remote control, it was obvious the restraints were proving effective. Both wheels were now rotating sweetly, while at the same time being held back when in the top position. But would the device move away from the vertical? The two cords were certainly holding the unit nice and steady, making it easy to spot the slightest sideways movement. I watched anxiously, my eyes fixed on the machine while my fingers operated the speed control. Then it moved. Slowly, but discernibly, the cage swung to the side until it had travelled about an inch. At that point it started oscillating to and fro due to the pulsing action of the gyros, but never once returning to its starting point. I was hypnotized by what the machine was doing and yet at the same time I was puzzled. There was something wrong.

Then it stuck me. The machine had moved backwards instead of forwards. It had gone negative instead of positive. This had also happened in the Melbourne laboratory. There my previous devices had started off by going downwards when they should have been going upwards. Again, as on that occasion, I was taken completely by surprise, not expecting the opposite to what was intended. Four more times I ran the machine. Each run was exactly the same as the one before; one inch backwards followed by oscillation, but always meeting that vital requirement of constant displacement from the vertical.

I knew, of course, from my previous experience that negative in this context was just as significant as positive. It was still inertial thrust no matter which direction it was taking. To all intents and purposes then, my machine had just successfully gone through the critical pendulum test. I should have been overjoyed, but I wasn't.

No engineer worth his salt likes to see any machine he has built go into reverse all the time. I'm too much of a purist to accept that. Only when I got the machine travelling in the right direction, and in the presence of at least one independent witness, would I be phoning up Harry Stine in Arizona and telling him that the Kidd Machine had crashed through his barrier.

Chapter 20

Somewhere in Europe, unbeknown to me, my name was being mentioned in royal circles. Not as idle chatter at court or in palace gossip, but at a much more serious and significant level. The Kidd Machine had seemingly caught the imagination of a member of a royal family, a working prince who had wide business interests and was particularly committed to supporting the development of new energy systems. He had been given a report on my work in the field of inertial propulsion and had expressed a wish to come to Dundee and see things for himself. Again, word of all this reached me through Ron Thompson, who had long since become the filter for such enquiries so as to give me a measure of privacy while working on my invention.

He had been up to his ankles in mud, cleaning out his fish pond, when his wife brought the phone out to the garden. It was a call from Canada, a consultant engineer, George Hathaway, ringing from his office in Toronto. He explained he was coming to Britain shortly with a client who wanted to meet me personally and talk about my machine. At that stage no hint was given of the client's identity. There seemed to be a wish to keep his name confidential for the time being. I was puzzled by this cloak and dagger affair but decided to go ahead with a meeting if only to find out who the mystery man was.

A few days later, however, through another phone call, I got to know his identity. Quite frankly, I thought at first it must be some kind of hoax. But then I was assured that my visitor was a real prince linked to a monarchy which stretched back many centuries to the times of the Holy Roman Empire. When I was told all this I was sworn to secrecy. His name was not to be revealed under any circumstances. In this matter he wished to remain as anonymous as possible, certainly wearing a hat rather than his crown and adopting the role of being the power behind the throne rather than the man up front taking the spotlight.

185

My oath of silence, however, did not extend to keeping Janet in the dark. We had never been in the habit of keeping secrets from each other and I certainly wasn't going to start now. My only reason for swithering over this one was knowing the state she would get into if I told her that Prince So-and-So of So-and-So would be paying us a visit in the near future. Can you imagine! But in the end I decided to tell her the full story. Her reaction was entirely predictable. 'Good heavens!' she shrieked. 'A prince? Coming here? Oh Sandy, what are we going to do?' I let her prattle on for a minute or two before interrupting in a tone of mock seriousness.

'Janet, we simply cannot have the house redecorated inside and out and a red carpet laid in time for the prince arriving,' I said. 'He is just going to have to put up with what we've got.'

Janet laughed. 'I didn't really mean that,' she replied. 'But how will I address him and what will I give him to eat?'

I told her not to worry about these things but to practise her curtseying instead. That only made matters worse. I then tried my best to play down the visit, but it was no use. She insisted on giving the house its second spring-clean of the year.

At last the great day dawned. Hathaway and the prince had flown up from London the previous evening, stayed the night in Edinburgh, and were driving through to Dundee first thing that morning. I had told them to make for the same hotel in the city where I had first met Noel Carroll, phone me, and I would come out with my car and lead them down to the house. When the call came just after breakfast-time I drove to the pick-up point where my two visitors were already waiting for me in hotel reception. We quickly introduced ourselves, then proceeded in convoy out of the city, driving along the banks of the Tay until reaching my house five miles away in the suburb of Barnhill. As I kept track of their hired car through my rear mirror I couldn't help thinking how surprised the civic fathers would have been to know they had a prince on their patch that day and hadn't been given the opportunity of offering him a little official hospitality.

When we arrived at my modest bungalow, Janet was hovering nervously behind the glass-panelled front door ready to welcome the guests. The prince was a tall, slim man, formally dressed. He was extremely courteous and rather reserved, but with a gentle, friendly manner which put Janet and me at ease from the moment he walked in and settled himself into a chair in the lounge. There was no fuss or formality and he was introduced without reference to the

186

royal connection. Like Ron Evans of British Aerospace before him he was travelling incognito.

We started by having a general discussion on the whole subject of gyroscopic propulsion and the part we thought it had to play in opening up the universe. Then we got down to my own involvement in this field. I explained how it had really begun when I had been thrown on my back by a spinning gyro while serving as a radar mechanic in the RAF and then, years later, being finally inspired to build my first machine after watching the Laithwaite lecture on television. I went on to relate everything that had happened to me since, although they already knew much of this from newspaper and magazine cuttings. After an hour we went through to the study to watch the Grampian documentary programme which allowed the visitors to see the original machine in action and follow its fortunes right through to the end of the university project. Most of the talking was done by Hathaway and myself with the prince listening intently, although frequently interrupting to ask his own searching questions.

In the midst of all this there arose a considerable domestic crisis. When offered mid-morning refreshments the prince would only accept a glass of iced water. Janet was in the kitchen preparing this very modest order when the front doorbell suddenly rang. When she opened the door there was a big delivery van right outside with two men busy unloading a settee and two easy chairs into the street. For a few seconds she couldn't understand what was happening. Then it struck her. Some time before we had ordered a new suite for the lounge and in the excitement of the prince's visit we had completely forgotten that it was due to be delivered that day.

At that moment Janet panicked. It had been arranged that the men would simply swop over one set of furniture for another and take the old suite away with them in the van. Janet now had this terrible vision of the men sweeping into the lounge and asking everyone, including a prince, to stand up while they changed over the seating! She had to think quickly on her feet. Going outside to the van Janet explained to the men that visitors had arrived unexpectedly from abroad for an important business meeting with her husband and as a great deal depended upon the outcome she couldn't possibly have them disturbed. This, of course, was all true. Fortunately the men had other deliveries to make in the district and said they would return in the afternoon. A most embarrassing situation had been avoided without the visitors being aware of the drama on the doorstep.

From the study we wandered through the kitchen and into the back garden where I pointed out my workshop in the tiny wooden shed. Although he had just seen it on the video, the prince was obviously taken aback when he saw for himself the cramped conditions I had been working in. He shook his head in amazement, no doubt thinking how he would have needed to fold his much bigger bulk almost in two to get into such a small space. Finally we moved into the garage where my latest machine was standing on the bench. Without revealing any of the latest technical detail, I gave them a breakdown of the various components and explained the general philosophy of the device. Then came all the inevitable questions.

By now I had grown accustomed to this routine. It was almost like a set tour; opening discussion in the lounge, video session in the study, a look at the garden shed workshop, then into the garage to examine the machine. I even suggested to Janet that we should have brochures printed! This visit, of course, had been motivated by much more than academic interest. Like Noel Carroll two years earlier, the prince was on a shopping expedition. He meant business. He was doing his round of inventors, ticking them off from a list supplied by the Advanced Energy Research Institute in London, and trying to decide whose ideas held the greatest promise for the future.

At last, after two and a half hours, they made to leave. Both men said they were impressed with everything they had seen and promised that I would be hearing from them again. They knew, of course, my obligations to BWN and even mentioned the possibility of a meeting with the Australians. I faxed Noel Carroll the following day to tell him exactly what had happened. I felt it would do him no harm to know that there was mounting interest elsewhere in the world over anti-gravity machines.

As the 'royal' car drove away from the house with Janet and I waving goodbye from the pavement, I wondered how many of our friends would have believed us if we had told them who had been in our home that day. We had no proof of the prince's identity. No business card. No snapshot. Our royal visitor had simply come and gone like a shadow, just as Noel Carroll had done nearly two years before. These visits by personages from foreign lands had been milestones in the life of the Kidd Machine, with this latest one having a fairytale touch. After

188

all, who has ever heard of a prince leaving his palace and travelling abroad to visit the humble workshop of an ordinary engineer just to look at his handiwork? It was an episode Janet and I would always remember.

Chapter 21

As the autumn of 1989 slipped gently into winter I continued to work feverishly on my machine in an effort to put it positively, and unequivocally, though the horizontal test. BWN had now made this my top priority. They were obviously anxious to have a reactionless device that could be demonstrated anywhere at the drop of a hat; portable proof of an anti-gravity force which could be seen by the naked eye, easily packaged and presented without having to resort to instrumentation and calculation as we had previously done in the Melbourne laboratory.

There was, of course, a certain irony in this latest endeavour. Whereas before all my efforts had been channelled into making my machine more efficient, I was now attempting to reduce its efficiency to meet the devilishly difficult conditions embodied in what appeared at first sight to be a simple test. As I have said already, my machine was designed to operate in the vertical mode where the gravitational forces on the gyros are equal and constant. By running it on its side this was no longer the case and I was now having to make the device asymmetrical to comply with these different circumstances. This meant I had to find the best way of neutralizing the effect of one of the gyros during each rotational movement of the machine. It was while I was still in the course of this long, painstaking task that Noel Carroll suddenly appeared on my doorstep at the beginning of September during a quick trip to London. He gave me a friendly clap on the back, told me to keep up the good work, then streaked off again over the horizon like Batman answering an SOS.

A couple of months later, again out of the blue, BWN called from Melbourne telling me to make my way immediately to California with my machine for a meeting with Noel, his brother Bob, and Mark Beran, the firm's consultant engineer in North America. I had to be in Pasadena within two days because Noel wanted to move quickly on to Tokyo on other business. I was simply told they wanted to observe my machine on the horizontal test, although at that stage I still hadn't completed all the adjustments necessary to give me the positive result I wanted.

While Janet started on the packing, I quickly dismantled the machine in the garage and stowed the parts away carefully in a padded case. My radio control unit posed a special problem. Since the Lockerbie air disaster in December 1988, in which 270 people were killed when a Pan Am jumbo jet was blown out of the sky above the small town in the Scottish Borders, airport security had been stepped up to unprecedented levels. Any suspicious baggage was being subjected to the keenest scrutiny. My radio unit, containing a transmitter with four wires each connected up to a battery, looked rather like an explosives device and was sure to cause a panic. What I had to do, therefore, was to sever the wires and tape them well back, showing clearly they were forming no contact. When I arrived at Edinburgh Airport for our shuttle flight to London, I immediately checked my machine and transmitter into security, explaining very carefully what it was and how I had immobilized the radio control unit. Finally everything went through and Janet and I were off on the first stage of our flight to Los Angeles.

By seven o'clock that evening, Californian time, we had reached our hotel in Pasadena. By then, of course, it was three o'clock the following morning in Britain. We had been on the move for twenty hours and were dog-tired, ready for bed. But because Noel was flying out to Japan first thing the following morning, I had to start preparing my machine right away for testing in the workshop attached to Bob Carroll's house. Within a couple of hours I had everything assembled and the wires soldered back on to the batteries in the transmitter.

We ran the tests for several hours, carrying out various speed adjustments until the machine was finally moving a couple of inches sideways in mid-air as it hung on the end of a cable suspended from the workshop roof. Disappointingly, however, it was swinging back again to its original vertical position after each pulsing movement, then moving forward once more when the next set of pulses came through. But under the strict rules that applied to the horizontal test the machine had to hold its position off the vertical all the time. There was no doubt, however, that the device was moving in a forward direction under inertial thrust. That had to be the case, given that the machine had nothing on which to react. It now seemed to me that the problem lay mainly in the rotational speed of the machine. It would have to produce a quicker pulsing movement to make sure it never fell back to its starting position. Once I achieve that, I will have taken another major step forward.

Noel, Bob, and Mark were all happy at what they had seen. 'You're almost there,' said Bob. 'A bit more to go and then we'll really have something to show the world.' By now it was three o'clock in the morning and after twenty-eight hours without sleep I collapsed into bed utterly exhausted.

Over the next few days we experimented with the machine on water, using the swimming pool at Bob's luxury home not far from Hollywood. We fixed a table top on to a couple of air beds, then anchored the device down on the flat surface with lumps of plasticine. When the gyros were revved up to a certain speed this bizarre-looking contraption began to move across the pool without the thrust of a propeller. Bob and Mark got quite excited when this happened, but as far as I was concerned the effect of air movement on both the machine and the water would invalidate any results obtained under such conditions out of doors. Nevertheless, it was all rather promising and by the time I left California a week later it had been decided that Janet and I would set up temporary home in the States early in 1990, while I undertook the next stage of development with the help of others. This would either take place in Pasadena with Bob Carroll or in Boulder with Mark Beran. It was simply the same project which had been scheduled to start twelve months before but was never implemented because of BWN's other commitments. Now everything seemed set to move forward at last.

While I had been working away in my own little world of gyroscopic inventions the eyes of the world at large had been focused on the remarkable events taking place in Eastern Europe. Solidarity had taken over the government of Poland, Hungarians were preparing for their first free elections in forty years, the Berlin Wall had been opened up, and throughout the Russian satellite states the Communist system was starting to crumble.

But something else had happened in Europe, too. Compared to these other epoch-making events it was totally unimportant but, for me at least, it was the only bit of news of any real, personal significance. It reached me through private channels and it concerned the prince who had been to my house earlier that year and whose name must still be kept confidential for diplomatic reasons. I had subsequently heard from his advisor, George Hathaway, that the prince was considering two possible options regarding the future development of my invention.

The first would have involved a straightforward funding operation for my machine under the supervision of the Advanced Energy Research Institute, but with possible collaboration of some kind with Scott Strachan, the Edinburgh engineer and inventor who was trail-blazing the same route as myself. The second proposition was to set up a foundation for research into advanced propulsion and energy concepts. Along with certain other selected inventors, I would be part of an elite consortium of radical innovators who would exchange ideas on an informal basis while continuing to forge ahead with their own projects. We would all be funded by the foundation during the development stages of our work and those of us who succeeded in achieving a commercial product would repay the prince by assigning a share of our profits to the central pool.

Whether such an arrangement would ever have worked out in practice is difficult to judge. Personally, I think it is unrealistic to expect inventors, even in the intellectual atmosphere envisaged by the prince, to speak freely about their work in the expectation that others won't copy their ideas. Human nature simply doesn't work like that. In any event, from what I was now being told, it was most unlikely that any of these moves would be going ahead, at least not in the foreseeable future. The prince – 'Our Prince' as Janet and I always referred to him as – would in future be having more important affairs of state on his plate and would not be able to sustain his interest in work like mine.

I was saddened by this turn of events. When you are battling to promote a controversial new concept every ally and potential avenue of support you can muster is worth its weight in gold. But often when one door closes another opens and that was exactly what was now happening from a most unexpected quarter.

★ ★ ★ ★ ★

Fred Scovell is a retired civil servant who lives quietly with his wife at Thames Ditton in Surrey, not far from Hampton Court. He entered government service as an honours graduate in engineering from Imperial College, London, and finished up as a principal scientific officer with the Admiralty. Like me he has had a long love-hate relationship with gyroscopes.

He first got to know of their idiosyncrasies in 1943 when

posted to the Torpedo Experimental Establishment at Greenock on the Clyde and vowed, as I had done at RAF Scampton, to someday invent a gyroscopic propulsion unit which would make the world sit up and take notice. It was 1975 before he started his experiments and when, twelve years later, he heard about my machine and the backing it had received from Dundee University and then BWN, he was spurred on to complete the design of his own inertial thrust device.

By the middle of 1988 he had filed an application for a patent and towards the end of that year he took the bull by the horns. Whereas I had been fearful that the Ministry of Defence might call in my application and commandeer my invention in the national interest, Fred Scovell marched down Whitehall waving his patent specification right under their noses. He offered the ministry a presentation of his anti-gravity device which, although only existing on paper, was supported by a simple piece of test apparatus which demonstrated a positive effect. Back came a reply from the scientific branch of the department saying they had consulted their external advisors. 'Their initial reaction,' said the letter, 'was to suggest that for an invention that invalidates one of the founding laws of classical mechanics they would expect a very detailed theoretical justification, including the axioms on which the calculation is based.'

However, the ministry offered Fred an audience with their scientists and that historic meeting duly took place. It lasted nearly three hours and the boffins seemed to be impressed with what he had to show them and the way he had put over his case. He has since had another letter from the ministry confirming their interest in his invention and holding out the possibility of financial support. Fred has been told that if he can find a university prepared to undertake a programme which will prove the theory and practicability of his device, then the ministry would consider giving such a project a measure of funding.

Although this offer may leave a lot to be desired from Scovell's point of view, I can assure him it represents a major shift in the government's attitude on this issue. In September 1987, when my Member of Parliament complained to the Secretary of State for Scotland about my work being allowed to go abroad through lack of indigenous support, he was more or less told that no one in their right mind would back a machine like mine where it was claimed such an invention broke the laws of physics. Now, eighteen months later, we have another branch of that same government almost pledging public

194

money to support the same kind of device as mine, one which poses similar threats to the same sacred theories.

Why this sudden change of heart? I am convinced the answer lies in my machine. It is because the Ministry of Defence, like British Aerospace and Rolls Royce, the Commonwealth Scientific Industrial Research Organization in Australia and no doubt other agencies in America, have been following the progress of my machine very closely and now realize it is not a gimmick, but something much more substantial and representative of a new scientific culture which can no longer be ignored. I believe it is on these grounds they have decided that Scovell's work should be given some sort of encouragement.

What Fred must do now is to find a university interested enough in his concept to lodge a tender with the Ministry of Defence for the funding necessary to carry out the experimental programme. I would suspect, after my university experience, that the academic institutions won't exactly fall over themselves with enthusiasm to get involved. Universities are where we are told you will find the experts. But the more expert a person is said to be the more reluctant they are to accept the viability of an anti-gravity machine, because if they do it means they have always been wrong before and, therefore, not an expert. They are not prepared to commit what they believe would be intellectual suicide by accepting even the possibility of an entirely new theory. I know this to be true and have the scars to prove it.

Fred says it could take up to £100,000 to build a prototype of his machine design. This may seem very little compared to most development budgets these days, but it is still only the first step and calls for a large measure of faith by your backer. BWN, who have been funding me for the past two and a half years, have still not actually crossed the Rubicon into the big-spending league. That, hopefully, will be happening shortly.

But as I look back now over the five years that have passed since I first emerged from my garden shed in November, 1984, I do so with an overwhelming sense of wonder. Although I knew my life would change drastically from the moment I claimed to have invented a revolutionary propulsion system, I could never have guessed that I would have been caught up in such an international web of high-powered events.

To have worked in Australia and America, to have gone from a humble workshop in a small suburb on the east coast of Scotland to a sophisticated laboratory in a teeming city on the south coast of Australia, has been an adventure beyond my wildest dreams. Along that incredible road my work has brought me into contact with five professors, six doctors, and a host of others in the fields of science and engineering. Patent applications for my device have been filed in Australia, America, Europe, Japan, Russia and Brazil. My machine has been the cause of controversy at government and United Nations level, the substance of complaint to the Press Council, and the subject of worldwide publicity through television, radio, magazines and newspapers. And now, of course, there is this book.

But all that is in the past. What of the future? Well, one thing is certain: the Kidd Machine is here to stay. Don't misunderstand me. What started off in my back garden still has a long way to go before finally convincing the world that we stand on the brink of realizing the greatest dream of all: manned flights to explore distant parts of the universe. Having a laboratory report which gives scientific backing to my machine is not the open-sesame I once thought it was going to be. There is still a lot of work to be done, barriers to be overcome, and deep-rooted prejudice to be whittled away. But those of us who believe so passionately in this new tomorrow are gradually making progress. The forces of change are slowly gathering strength.

This is, after all, what people want all over the world. When the government minister said in his letter about my machine that Newton's laws had served mankind well for the past three hundred years he was perfectly right. The public don't complain about Newton and Einstein in the way they do about inflation and congestion on the roads. But that's hardly the point. People know that, with man having already been into space, the universe is out there waiting to be discovered. They can see the stars beckoning in the heavens and deep down they are excited at the prospect of conquering these distant shores. It has always been that way.

Now let me put into perspective the part I believe I have played in furthering the cause of anti-gravity propulsion. Others had designed and patented inertial thrust machines before I arrived on the scene. But my work captured the public imagination on an unprecedented scale because of the way it was packaged and promoted and publicized. Without this exposure my machine would never have gained credibility and through that the respectability of commercial support. I was forced to put my ideas across through the popular media because there was no way the scientific journals would ever publish any paper of mine.

As I have described earlier, all this publicity has encouraged other inventors to come forward with their devices in a new mood of assertive self-confidence. I have become the rallying point in this drive towards new scientific frontiers. It has taken over my life; Janet's too, because she has supported me constantly. Nothing will ever make me give up now.

So far I have built seven machines. If need be, I'll build another seventy. I am more convinced than ever that finding the means of powering a flying saucer is my pre-ordained role in life and history will eventually tell the part I played in changing the world. I leave you with a message from Theodore Roosevelt, a former American President. He said these words once in 1910. I say them every day:

It is not the critic who counts;
not the man who points out where the strong man stumbled
or where the doer of deeds could have done better.
The credit belongs to the man who is actually in the arena;
whose face is marred by dust and sweat and blood;
who strives valiantly,
who errs and comes short again and again;
who knows the great enthusiasms;
who, at the best, knows the triumph of high achievement;
and who, at the worst, if he fails, at least fails while daring greatly,
so that his place shall never be with those cold and timid souls,
who knew neither victory nor defeat.

Appendix

Measurement of force generation of a prototype gyroscope invention

INTRODUCTION

BWN Vortoil Pty. Ltd. have been working with an inventor, Mr. Alexander Kidd of Sandra Systems, on the development of a prototype device to convert rotational energy into lineal force by gyroscopic means. Past trials of this device have involved external mechanical restraints which have left some doubt regarding whether the result of a nett 'lift' force was conclusive or not.

Consequently, Vipac Pty. Ltd. was commissioned to build a load measuring system to test the unit, without any restraint other than the cord supporting it. We were also commissioned to analyse the measured test data and report on the findings.

The tests were conducted at Vipac's Melbourne laboratories over the period 1-3 March, 1988.

DESCRIPTION OF DEVICE

The device consists of a pair of flywheels each rotating at the same speed about a horizontal axis. This pair of flywheels rotate together (on opposite sides) about a vertical axis at a lower speed. Cams cyclically displace the flywheels away from the vertical axis; they return under their own gyroscopic effect.

In the form tested, drive about both axes was provided by a model aircraft engine, geared down by a spur gear train and belt. The whole self-contained drive and gyroscope assembly was mounted in a wooden box which could be suspended by a single cord from above. The upper half of the box, containing the gyroscope, was divided from the lower half containing the engine, and was fully enclosed to eliminate nett aerodynamic effects.

The exhaust of the engine was fed out through the side of the box. The mass flow egress from the exhaust could be thought to apply torque to the whole box. This, however, was not observed: the two light strings attached horizontally to the box remained *slack* at all times, except when the engine was accelerating.

TEST STRATEGY

The fundamental aim of the test was to determine whether the unit provided a nett positive force, i.e. whether the 'up' force pulses were, on average, larger than the 'down' force pulses. The inventor expected a margin of 'a few ounces', or about 1% of the box static weight.

To test this hypothesis, it was decided to hang the box by a single cord from a custom strain-gauge-based measurement beam. The dynamic signal from this load cell could then be statistically processed in a variety of ways by a commercial Signal Analyser.

INSTRUMENTATION

The following instrumentation was used to conduct the measurements:

load cell:	custom aluminium cantilever beam fitted with 4-arm strain bridge (2 gauges on upper surface and 2 gauges on lower surface);
strain amplifier:	applied measurement, 10 channel;
signal analysers:	1) Hewlett Packard, 2 channel, model 5423A; 2) Ono Sokki, 2 channel, model CF350;
hard copy:	Hewlett Packard, digital plotter, model 7470A;
data recorder:	TEAC, 4 channel FM data recorder, model R61;

accelerometer:	Bruel and Kjaer, model 4369;
charge amplifier:	Bruel and Kjaer, model 2635;
accelerometer calibrator:	Bruel and Kjaer, model 4291.

TEST PROCEDURE: INITIAL SET-UP

As the mass of the box would change during a test run due to fuel being consumed, both the strain amplifier and signal analysers were set to AC coupling, i.e. the DC, or static, component of the signal was removed. Prior to this, however, the polarity of the measurement system was established by adding a small mass to the box. 'Down' was confirmed as being negative, and 'up' as positive.

The expected maximum flywheel-pair rotation speed was 8 Hz, and so the load beam had been designed to have a fundamental natural frequency as far above this as possible without too much compromise in sensitivity. Prior to testing, this was checked by lightly tapping the box vertically: the lowest measured natural frequency was 15.2 Hz.

The accelerometer was attached to the bottom of the box below the estimated position of the centre of mass.

BACKGROUND MEASUREMENT

The (approximately) 5.5 kg box hanging by the Kevlar cord on the load beam essentially formed a very sensitive servo accelerometer. Therefore, there was signal output even when the unit was not running.

To establish the background signal level, the HP5423 analyser was set to the voltage range expected for the test measurement, and to 50 Hz bandwidth, histogram, 50 linear sum averages. These settings correspond to fifty 2.56 second overlapped data samples, or about one minute of data.

The result of this measurement was a Probability Density Function (PDF) or histogram. The PDF was then integrated to yield the Cumulative Density Function (CDF). Using the analyser cursor, the 50 percentile value of the distribution (i.e. the median) was then read off. The analyser is a digital instrument with fixed resolution and so, in practice, the 50 percentile was read off as *two* values: the nearest points above and below the 50.000 percentile.

The 50 percentile (or median) value was chosen as the basic parameter of measurement because it represents the value which has half of the PDF below it and half above it. Note that the median is equivalent to the mean or 'average' if the PDF has a normal distribution, but is different if the PDF is skewed. Thus, by measuring the 50 percentile we could determine if there was a change in bias of positive and negative forces between background and test, even if these two cases had different shaped PDFs.

The background measurement was also repeated *after* each test run.

FORCE CALIBRATION

All measurements of force on the load beam were conducted in Volts. However, to obtain an indication of force in Newtons an approximate calibration was conducted. This was done by weighing 7 small identical 11.34 gram masses on a beam balance, DC coupling the strain amplifier and analyser, and measuring the averaged voltage amplitude of the DC (0 Hz) line on the spectrum for each mass loading. This was repeated twice.

The sixteen data points were then curve-fitted to yield the result:

$$\text{Grams (force)} = -0.62 \times \text{mV} \; or \; 63 \; \text{mV/N}$$

The accuracy of this figure is estimated to be within $\pm$ 10% and so should be used only for indicative purposes.

PRELIMINARY MEASUREMENTS

A series of seventeen preliminary trial runs were conducted during which voltage ranges were determined and during which the inventor changed the size and mass of the flywheels until he was happy with the 'sound' of the unit. The preliminary trials also revealed problems of drive belt slip, which may be best illustrated by reference to *Figures 1 and 2*.

Figure 1 shows a typical test PDF. It may be seen that the

202

distribution is saddle-shaped and reached a positive peak of 1.664 Volts (approx. 26.4 N). *Figure 2*, by contrast, was recorded during a test when the belt was slipping (i.e. only intermittent drive to the flywheel pair). It may be seen that the highest positive peak is much lower than *Figure 1* (around 1 Volt) and that the force spends considerable proportionate time near zero amplitude due to the lack of consistent drive.

The belt slip phenomenon is much more evident from the PDF's than from the corresponding CDF's in *Figures 3 and 4*.

TEST MEASUREMENTS

After the teething problems had been overcome, the formal test series was conducted. It was decided that 20 runs would be carried out in a nominally identical manner. These were Runs 18 to 39, of which two (Nos. 20 and 24) had to be rejected because the device was touched during the test to prevent engine overspeed.

Procedure for each test comprised:

1. Taking a background PDF measurement with analyser: AC coupled, 50 Hz bandwidth, 50 averages, ± 2.5 V range generally. Simultaneously tape-recording load beam force and box acceleration.
2. Starting engine.
3. Taking test PDF measurement (settings as above), live and simultaneously tape-recording.
4. Stopping engine.
5. Repeating background PDF measurement.
6. Integrating PDF's to generate CDF's.
7. Reading off the voltage values at data points either side of the 50 percentile point.

RESULTS

The raw results of the 20 test runs are tabulated in Appendix 1. From this tabulation, it is evident that for all twenty tests the device did apparently provide a positive 'lift' force. It is also evident that there is significant spread of results, albeit all positive. This would be in part due to the fact that the unit's speed was not matched between runs: it was only set (by the inventor) by ear.

As the accelerometer could not be positioned at the exact (unknown) centre of mass of the box, the Transfer Function between force and acceleration was not a constant value, i.e. mass of the box. The Transfer Function was frequency-dependent, indicating that rigid-body modes of the box (rocking, pitching, yawing, etc.) were shaping the acceleration response. Therefore the accelerometer data has not assisted us in determining the test results.

The results are best examined by expressing the bias or 'lift' as a percentage of the peak force generated (the 99 percentile has been used to express the 'peak'); the average result of the 20 tests was *2.2%*.

Whereas 'lift' force as a percentage of peak force is a useful measure, because it is independent of the device mass, it gives no indication of absolute value. Column B of Appendix 1 shows that the average absolute force over the 20 runs was *0.51 N* (= 52 grams force = 1.8 ounces force). This corresponds (column C) to approximately *1%* of the unit static weight.

All of the above figures are based on linear interpolation of the exact 50.000 percentile value from the adjacent data points immediately above and below this value. As shall be discussed in greater detail later, immediate questions arise whenever interpolated results are used. Therefore, column D in Appendix 1 was computed. This column represents the 'worst case', by using the *lowest* of the two '50 percentile' test values in conjunction with the *highest* of the four '50 percentile' background values. The end result is changed only marginally: the mean 'lift' force as a percentage of the 'peak' (99 percentile) force drops from *+2.2% to +2.0%*, but *remains non-zero*.

EVALUATION OF RESULTS: RESOLUTION

The HP5423 analyser is a digital instrument and so has finite voltage resolution. It is not necessary to pursue an analysis of the effect of this resolution, because column D in Appendix 1 is based on comparison of the *lowest* of the two *test* data points around its exact 50.000 percentile with the *highest* of the *background* data points around its 50.000 percentile. The result, as shown in Appendix 1, was that all tests still yielded positive values.

ACCURACY

The tests were deliberately structured so that there was no requirement for *absolute* accuracy of voltage measurement, force calibration, etc. Thus, the test reduced to determining whether the 50 percentile values of the test measurements were different from the background measurements, i.e. whether the device produced a 'bias' in the expected positive (up) direction.

To this end all tests were conducted *without changing the settings on any measuring instrument* between the test run and the two respective background measurements before and after each test run. This ensured that *relative* results could be compared exactly.

STATISTICAL EVALUATION

It had been intended to conduct a statistical evaluation of the confidence level associated with the basic '20 out of 20' outcome of the tests.

The appropriate test to use for comparing the means of two small samples of data (background and test) is the 't' test. However, this test requires that the two samples be drawn from populations which are normally distributed (i.e. Gaussian) *and* that the two samples have the same variance.

While the background data is essentially Gaussian, it may be seen from *Figure 1* that the test data certainly is *not*. This is due to the very nature of the device, which has a cyclic mechanism to produce force pulses of similar magnitude. Although the test force peaks are not, by simple inspection, normally distributed, it is important to note that the twenty 50 percentile values *may* be normally distributed. This is discussed in the next section.

Nevertheless, as shown in Appendix 1, the test and background data sets have very different variances and so the 't' test could not be used.

CONFIDENCE LEVELS OF FINAL RESULTS

The test results in Appendix 1 showed a positive (non-zero) outcome in all 20 cases. However, one ultimately wants to know whether, if 1000 tests were conducted, would the result be 1000 out of 1000?

Some measure of confidence can be obtained by first testing the results (column A, Appendix 1) to determine if they are normally distributed, and then using statistical inference.

TEST FOR NORMALITY

The procedure used involved the following steps:

a. Calculate estimates for mean and standard deviation of population.
b. Divide the twenty readings into groups, satisfying the requirement that there must be at least five values per group.*
c. Calculate the Chi-squared statistic from the expected and observed values.
d. Compare the Chi-squared statistic to the Chi-squared distribution to determine the level of confidence.

This procedure is shown in Appendix 1. The number of degrees of freedom (DOF) is 1 and is calculated thus: no. of groups (4) − 1 (by definition) − 1 (because population mean is estimated, not known − 1 (because population s.d. is estimated, not known) = 1. The resulting Chi-squared statistic is 1.6. Now, for DOF the Chi-squared distribution gives:*

$$70\% \text{ confidence level} = 1.074$$
$$80\% \text{ confidence level} = 1.642$$
$$90\% \text{ confidence level} = 2.706$$

As the actual calculated value is 1.6, the finding is that we are very close to *80%* confident that the column A data has a normal distribution.

* Hoel, P. G., *Introduction to Mathematical Statistics*

INFERENCE

From column A, Appendix 1, we have:

> Maximum = 5.0%
> Minimum = 0.6%
> Mean = 2.2%
> Sample Standard Deviation = 1.13%

The hypothesis we wish to examine is that the probability of the population from which the 20 sample tests were drawn has a mean of zero, i.e. the 20 tests yielded a mean result of +2.2%, but is this a 'fluke': if a very large number of tests were conducted could the mean be zero?

So, we wish to determine:

$$P\{\bar{X} \leq O\} = P\left\{\frac{\bar{X} - Ms}{S-} \leq \frac{2.2 - 0}{1.13}\right\}$$

where $\bar{X}$ = mean to be tested (= 0)
Ms = Sample mean, actual (= 2.2)
$S-$ = Sample standard deviation (= 1.13)
$P\{\}$ = denotes probability

$$\frac{\bar{X} - Ms}{S-} = Z = \text{Standard normal variable} = \text{no. of standard deviations}$$

$$\rightarrow P\{\bar{X} \leq 0\} = P\{Z \leq 1.95\}$$

As the number of samples is not infinite, we cannot use the Normal Distribution tables to evaluate the probability of $Z \leq$ 1.95 standard deviations: the correct distribution is Student's t Distribution. Consulting standard tables,* we find that the probability that the population mean will be as low as zero, given 20 samples, Ms = 2.2 and $S-$ = 1.13 is *0.033*. (For a Normal Distribution, the result would have been 0.026, not substantially different.)

It then follows:

* Hoel, P. G., *Introduction to Mathematical Statistics*

1. There is only a small chance (3.3% probability) that the sample mean result of +2.2% is drawn from a population of results with mean zero.
2. We are 96.7% confident that a measured non-zero result is correct.

The above result indicates a high level of confidence in the non-zero outcome of the test series. However, it must be remembered that the above inference is based on the assumption of a Normal Distribution of the sample means, and that we are only 80% confident that the distribution of sample means is in fact normal. Therefore, the above figure of 96.7% should be multiplied by 0.8, yielding a composite confidence level of $96.7 \times 0.8 = 77.4\%$.

i.e. The final confidence level in the non-zero test outcome is 77%.

COMMENTS

1. The speed of the engine was not controlled during the tests. If it were, then we contend that the spread of results would have been less (lower standard deviation) and the 96.7% inferred confidence level would have been higher.
2. We calculated 80% confidence that the '% of peak force' results were normally distributed. To increase this confidence level would require a substantially higher number of tests (say 100, to give 10 ranges values, rather than the 4 used for the normality test).
3. A rigorous statistical testing of results would involve a *joint probability* approach using three sets of values (background before, test, background after), and first establishing normality confidence for each set. However, this would only be worthwhile if one were working with a larger number of tests than the 20 available.

CONCLUSION

A series of twenty identical tests were conducted on a prototype gyroscopic invention to determine whether it could produce a non-zero mean force bias.

The results have shown that:

1. The force 'bias' was non-zero for all 20 tests.
2. The average force 'bias' generated amounted to approximately 2% of the highest force peaks.
3. The average force 'bias' generated amounted to approximately *1%* of the unit static weight, or approximately *0.5 N*.
4. The final statistical confidence level of the non-zero force bias outcome was *77%*.

March 1988

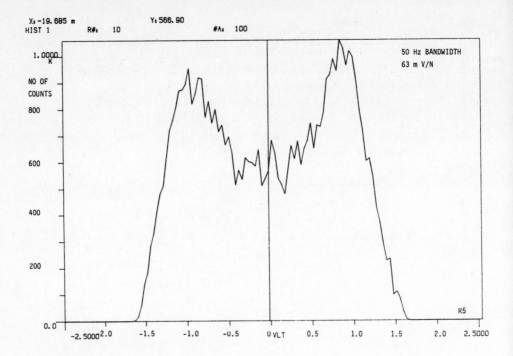

Figure 1: Histogram (PDF) for Typical Test – Characteristic Saddle Shape

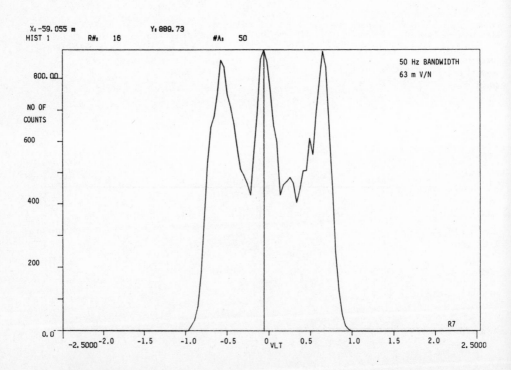

Figure 2: Histogram for Test with Belt Slipping – Note High No. of Counts near Zero Volts

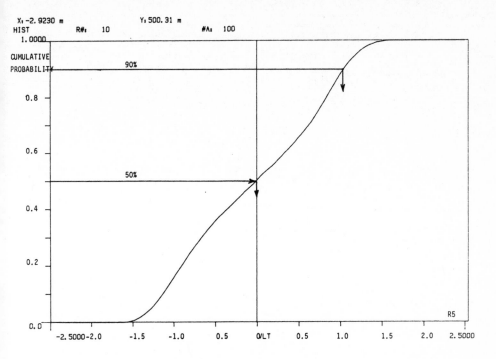

Figure 3: CDF from Figure 1 (Typical 'Good' Test)

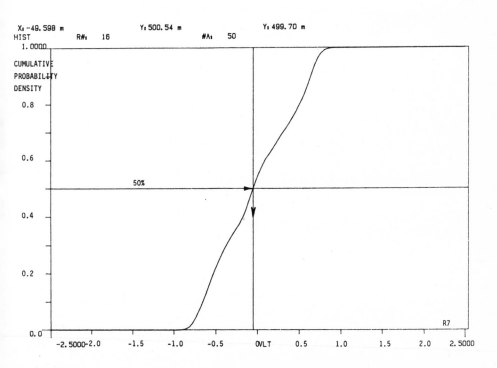

Figure 4: CDF from Figure 2 (Test During which Belt Slip Occurred)

VIPAC PTY.LTD.   BWN VORTOIL GYRO FORCE MEASUREMENT RESULTS

RUN NO.	BACKGROUND BEFORE TEST: LOWER : 50 % %ile	volts	50 PERCENTILE INTERPOLATED LEVEL volts	UPPER : 50 % %ile	volts	TEST: LOWER : 50 % %ile	volts	50 PERCENTILE INTERPOLATED LEVEL volts	UPPER : 50 % %ile	volts	99 % volts	BACKGROUND AFTER TEST: LOWER : 50 % %ile	volts	50 PERCENTILE INTERPOLATED VALUE volts	UPPER : 50 % %ile	volts	A "LIFT" FORCE % OF PEAK	B "LIFT" FORCE N	C "LIFT" FORCE % OF WT.	D WORST CASE % OF PEAK
18	0.49691	-0.03501	-0.03486	0.52614	-0.03355	0.49998	0.00583	0.00590	0.50039	0.00729	1.2631	0.47137	-0.03647	-0.03505	0.50076	-0.03501	+ 3.2%	0.65	1.2%	+ 3.1%
19	0.48873	-0.03792	-0.03742	0.52131	-0.03647	0.49941	-0.01897	-0.01758	0.50003	-0.01751	0.9962	0.49031	-0.03647	-0.03601	0.52095	-0.03501	+ 1.9%	0.30	0.6%	+ 1.6%
20																				
21	0.48717	-0.03355	-0.03286	0.51412	-0.03209	0.49990	-0.00730	-0.00692	0.50029	-0.00584	1.6248	0.48899	-0.03647	-0.03594	0.51940	-0.03501	+ 1.7%	0.44	0.8%	+ 1.5%
22	0.48154	-0.03647	-0.03558	0.51162	-0.03501	0.50000	-0.00292	-0.00292	0.50000	-0.00292	1.5141	0.48103	-0.03501	-0.03403	0.50932	-0.03355	+ 2.1%	0.51	0.9%	+ 2.0%
23	0.48978	-0.03355	-0.03298	0.51587	-0.03209	0.49984	-0.02188	-0.02112	0.50030	-0.01969	1.9239	0.47322	-0.03647	-0.03597	0.50280	-0.03592	+ 0.7%	0.21	0.4%	+ 0.5%
24																				
25	0.48687	-0.03355	-0.03284	0.51392	-0.03209	0.49970	0.02771	0.02844	0.50030	0.02917	1.2514	0.49193	-0.03647	-0.03609	0.52267	-0.03501	+ 5.0%	1.00	1.9%	+ 4.8%
26	0.49941	-0.03647	-0.03644	0.53062	-0.03501	0.49993	-0.00876	-0.00860	0.50060	-0.00730	1.1391	0.47433	-0.03501	-0.03366	0.50201	-0.03355	+ 2.3%	0.42	0.8%	+ 2.2%
27	0.49934	-0.03938	-0.03936	0.52866	-0.03793	0.49986	0.02771	0.02821	0.50027	0.02917	1.6642	0.49692	-0.03647	-0.03633	0.52797	-0.03501	+ 4.0%	1.05	1.9%	+ 3.8%
28	0.48148	-0.04084	-0.04011	0.51852	-0.03938	0.49972	-0.01969	-0.01925	0.50018	-0.01897	1.8538	0.47451	-0.03793	-0.03675	0.50613	-0.03647	+ 1.0%	0.30	0.6%	+ 0.9%
29	0.48039	-0.03792	-0.03704	0.51242	-0.03647	0.49967	0.02041	0.02132	0.50020	0.02187	1.8626	0.48066	-0.03355	-0.03249	0.50723	-0.03209	+ 3.0%	0.89	1.6%	+ 2.8%
30	0.49750	-0.03355	-0.03342	0.52513	-0.03209	0.49979	-0.02334	-0.02280	0.50035	-0.02188	1.2514	0.49300	-0.03648	-0.03518	0.50090	-0.03501	+ 0.9%	0.18	0.3%	+ 0.7%
31	0.47144	-0.03647	-0.03506	0.50090	-0.03501	0.49967	-0.00584	-0.00500	0.50024	-0.00438	1.6949	0.47307	-0.03501	-0.03360	0.50090	-0.03355	+ 1.7%	0.47	0.9%	+ 1.6%
32	0.49139	-0.03664	-0.03619	0.52210	-0.03501	0.49948	0.01604	0.01678	0.50050	0.01750	1.3623	0.48848	-0.03355	-0.03293	0.51555	-0.03209	+ 3.8%	0.81	1.5%	+ 3.5%
33	0.47505	-0.03792	-0.03678	0.50672	-0.03647	0.49942	-0.02334	-0.02191	0.50001	-0.02188	1.4163	0.47368	-0.03793	-0.03671	0.50523	-0.03647	+ 1.0%	0.24	0.4%	+ 0.9%
34	0.48819	-0.03647	-0.03591	0.51870	-0.03501	0.49981	-0.00438	-0.00389	0.50037	-0.00292	1.5257	0.47652	-0.03512	-0.03378	0.50391	-0.03355	+ 2.0%	0.49	0.9%	+ 1.9%
35	0.48186	-0.03501	-0.03405	0.50932	-0.03355	0.49997	0.00729	0.00769	0.50008	0.00875	1.7649	0.49372	-0.03064	-0.03026	0.51794	-0.02918	+ 2.3%	0.63	1.2%	+ 2.1%
36	0.49108	-0.03792	-0.03753	0.52382	-0.03647	0.49975	0.00145	0.00218	0.50025	0.00291	1.5388	0.48072	-0.03793	-0.03705	0.51277	-0.03647	+ 2.6%	0.63	1.2%	+ 2.5%
37	0.49314	-0.03501	-0.03467	0.52215	-0.03355	0.49967	-0.00146	-0.00069	0.50003	-0.00062	1.5855	0.48538	-0.03501	-0.03426	0.51393	-0.03355	+ 2.1%	0.54	1.0%	+ 2.0%
38	0.49669	-0.03355	-0.03338	0.52429	-0.03209	0.49991	-0.02772	-0.02759	0.50089	-0.02626	1.1801	0.49855	-0.03501	-0.03494	0.52780	-0.03355	+ 0.6%	0.10	0.2%	+ 0.4%
39	0.47090	-0.03647	-0.03503	0.50033	-0.03501	0.49980	-0.01313	-0.01255	0.50030	-0.01168	1.3886	0.47171	-0.03793	-0.03662	0.50315	-0.03647	+ 1.7%	0.37	0.7%	+ 1.6%

	Background before test	Test	Background after test
MAXIMUM =	-32.84 mV	28.44 mV	-30.26 mV
MINIMUM =	-40.11 mV	-27.59 mV	-37.05 mV
MEAN =	-35.57 mV	-3.01 mV	-34.88 mV
SAMPLE STD. DEVN. =	2.08 mV	16.97 mV	1.75 mV
SAMPLE VARIANCE =	4.33 mV^2	288.01 mV^2	3.06 mV^2
POPN. STD. DEVN. =	2.03 mV	16.54 mV	1.71 mV

	A	B	C	D
MAX =	5.0%			
MIN =	0.6%			
MEAN=	2.2%	0.51	0.9%	+ 2.0%
PSD =	1.1%			

OVERALL BACKGROUND STATISTICS:

MEAN = -35.229 mV
STANDARD DEVIATION OF SAMPLE= 1.929 mV
VARIANCE = 3.722 mV^2

LEGEND:

COLUMN A= "LIFT" EXPRESSED AS A PERCENTAGE OF INTERPOLATED 50%ile (TEST VOLTAGE-MEAN BACKGROUND VOLTAGES)/(99%ile TEST VOLTAGE)
i.e. THE "BIAS" FORCE AS A PROPORTION OF THE "PEAK" FORCE. ***NOTE: PSD= ESTIMATE FOR POPULATION STANDARD DEVIATION.
COLUMN B= "LIFT" FORCE IN NEWTONS, USING INTERPOLATED 50%ile VALUES AND ASSUMING APPROXIMATE FORCE CALIBRATION OF 63mV/N
COLUMN C= "LIFT" FORCE EXPRESSED AS A PERCENTAGE OF APPROXIMATE UNIT WEIGHT (5.5kg)
COLUMN D= WORST CASE "LIFT" FORCE, AS A PERCENTAGE OF 99%ile FORCE
i.e. (LOWEST "50%ile" TEST VOLTAGE - HIGHEST "50%ile" BACKGROUND VOLTAGE)/99%ile TEST VOLTAGE

TEST FOR NORMALITY OF COLUMN A

GAUSS	RANGES	OBSERVED	EXPECTED	RESULT
-0.67448	0.01421	5	5	0
0	0.02184	7	5	0.8
0.674489	0.02947	3	5	0.8
		5	5	0
		20	20	

CHI STATISTIC 1.6

GAUSS= NORMAL DISTRIBUTION TABLES
RANGES= GAUSS*PSD+MEAN
RESULT= (OBSERVED-EXPECTED)^2/EXPECTED

NOTE: VALUE OF CHI-SQUARED DISTRIBUTION FOR ONE D.O.F. AND 80% CONFIDENCE IS 1.642. THEREFORE WE ARE 80% CONFIDENT THAT COLUMN A IS NORMALLY DISTRIBUTED.

Appendix 1: Raw and Reduced Test Results